From Whence My Strength Comes

Lucille Feggens Sharpe Reddick, my mother

From Whence My Strength Comes

Georgianna Sommerset

To my cousin Beverly

Georgianna Sommerset

8/30/08

WILLIAMS & COMPANY
BOOK PUBLISHERS

ISBN 1-878853-90-2

This book is dedicated to the memory of my mother, Lucille Feggens Sharpe Reddick

Chapter One

THE SUN IS BEGINNING to go down as I sit visiting with my eighty-five year old father. I am sitting on the porch, looking down the long road that leads up to the house, my mind full of the joys, pains and sorrows that come and go in quick flashes.

It has been forty-five years since I lived on this farm. There were times when living in this house would make me feel important, when I would dream and dream and pretend that I was better than the sharecroppers and their children who worked for my grandfather and father. But even in those days I knew that in many ways they were better off than I was.

I am fifty-seven years old now. I have been married for thirty-eight years and have two daughters, one a doctor and the other an investment banker. In spite of all the good things that have happened to me in my later life, somewhere deep down within me I harbor an indelible dislike for my father that I have never been able to let go of. As you read more of this story you will begin to understand the reasons for this.

It is a hundred miles, one way, to the farm. Either my brother or I drive this distance once a week to see that Daddy's needs are met. I do this simply because it is the right thing to do, but the past continues to eat me alive. Daddy hasn't changed much at eighty-five. The only real change I see is that he is old. He continues to drink, use snuff, and enjoy women when opportunity knocks. When I arrive he sometimes forgets who I am and that I am his daughter, not just another woman that he can amuse himself with. When I remind him who I am, he apologizes for his behavior and pretends he was just teasing.

Toney is three years older than I am. He is a short, passive, and prone to ill health. When I was a girl, I felt that Toney was Mama's favorite. He could never do anything wrong in her eyes. I always felt that my aunts on my father's side liked him better than they did me. In spite of his shortcomings, Toney had one thing that I did not have: light skin. My aunts called me ugly and black and laughed at me. Perhaps they did not think I would remember, but they were wrong. I remember all of this quite well.

Everyone would share with Toney, sometimes because he was Grandmother's driver when everyone was working in the field or Daddy was running around with the ladies and wouldn't take her to handle her business.

Toney was thirteen years old, had no license, but was a very good driver. The sheriff wouldn't stop them because they knew Grandma and knew Grandma was rich and powerful, as far as power went for blacks at that time. They stopped them on occasion if they had a county patrol on that didn't know that it was Aunt Mary Ann in the car (that is what they called her).

The only time Daddy gave Grandma any real time was when it was time to take resin to Hazelhurst to be sold or take tobacco or cotton to market or maybe sell some trees. He would be there any time money was to be had, because he was surely going to get some of it.

We went to bed with our clothes on because we knew he might beat the hell out of us, and we would have to run for our lives. Mom was afraid to have him put in jail because he would only stay overnight and then come right back to beat her up for putting him in jail.

Why should he stay in jail when his parents owned two thousand acres of land, with plenty of pine trees, cotton, fruit trees, and anything else you could name? They also had their own sharecroppers.

Grandma would buy her children out of any trouble they got into, which meant she had a bunch of unruly children. The boys were womanizers.

Grandma's oldest son, Willie, and the second oldest son, John, and their families lived up the lane less than a half a mile from each other. They often enjoyed Friday and Saturday nights together along with Freddie, who was married to Uncle Willie's daughter.

One particular weekend things got out of control. Daddy was roasting sweet potatoes in the fire place, under the ashes, and Mama was entertaining us by making shadow figures on the wall with her hands while Toney and I tried to guess what the figures were. Daddy, dipping snuff, was laughing and joking. The kerosene lamp light and the light from the fire place added a warm family feeling to the room.

Suddenly we were disturbed by an unearthly banging on

the front door. Outside, It was raining and thundering. Flashes of lightning were everywhere. The knock on the door was so hard that my parents jumped, as did Toney and I. Daddy rushed to the door, pulling it open. It was Auntie Carrie, Daddy's sister. She looked wild and strange, as if she had just seen a ghost. She had no shoes on, no hat on and was soaking wet from the rain. Her eyes seemed as if they had grown larger. I could see that something had frightened her. She could hardly talk so that we could understand what she was saying, but I knew that something serious was wrong, because no one lived close enough just to run next door in all that rain.

Just as we were about to eat our fresh-roasted sweet potatoes, Auntie stepped inside the door from the porch smelling like fresh, uncleaned chitterlings. She had been at the creek earlier cleaning chitterlings, and I thought to myself how much I hated that smell.

"Sun," Auntie Carrie called to Daddy, "Papa, wants you to take Mama up the lane. Something bad has happened. "Cooter," Daddy answered Auntie Carrie, "get in here before the lighting strikes you. Something is always happening up that lane. "

The front door was still open, and I could hear the rain beating on the tin roof. "Give me a damn minute," Daddy said, as he put his shoes on and grabbed a coat and hat. He was not in a hurry, as though he knew what he would find.

"Why couldn't all of this have happened tomorrow?" I thought to myself. "Aunt Carrie just messed up a rare family moment at our house. What I found out the next day was that

Cousin Freddie was dead. I thought that there must be more to it than that. Why would all the adults go running up the lane? But none of the grown-ups were talking so the kids could hear. Very soon Fred's family moved away. Shortly afterwards, John's family moved away, too. This was all so strange.

I often enjoyed having to spend a lot of time around Mama. I was considered too young to do much work in the field, which meant I got a chance to overhear conversations of Mama's. These were especially interesting if she trusted the person she was talking to. Mama and her best friend Martha talked about a lot of things—mostly about Daddy and the women in his life or Daddy's family, and how thieving his sisters and brothers were.

Martha was a beautician. On her day off she and Mama would often wash each other's hair if she could manage it without Daddy knowing. He didn't want her to leave home to go to anyone's house. He made us sweep the yards before he left home and when he got home, he would search the smooth yard for foot prints that weren't Mama's, Toney's or mine. I heard Mama tell her friend about the night it rained so hard, about all the screaming and crying, and how they found cousin Freddie face down in the mud with his throat cut. She told how Uncle John's wife and Freddie were each other's sweethearts. She told how the daughter tried to rob cousin Freddie, and things got out of control because they were drunk. No one ever made a day in jail, but Uncle John's family had to leave the state.

Chapter Two

MAMA WAS ALWAYS AFRAID. She told Toney and me often when she missed a sharecropper that had no family and just sort of wandered on the land or from place to place. She would say, "They have killed another one to keep from paying him, because I haven't seen him in weeks. They will kill us too if we are not careful," Mama said. She said that was why we couldn't tell anyone about the way we were being treated.

That night we stayed over at my grandparents' (my father's parents) house. It was unusual for my mother to want to stay overnight. My brother never really minded. I thought our staying there was strange, because we only lived past the barn and down the hill. Well, it had rained the night before, and this is clay country. Once you got down there in the truck, the only way anyone could get out was to walk across the corn field and through the pecan orchard.

When morning came, Mama and I walked down the hill holding hands to keep me from stepping in all that wet clay and slipping down. I had not yet seen Daddy that morning. The closer we came to where we lived, I could see smoke. As we came closer, I could see that the house was gone, burned down to ashes. I became so frightened, frantic about where would we live. Our house was gone, the only house I ever remembered living in. It had been a three-room country farm house with wooden windows that we opened every morning and closed every night; we locked them with a piece of string that we tied on a nail. The doors were locked with small pieces of wood with a nail driven through the middle of them.

I looked at Mama's face as she kicked around in the ashes as though looking for something special. I asked "Where is Daddy?" I knew that my brother was alright, because we had left him at Grandmother's.

"You see those piles of ashes over there? That's him," Mama said . My heart dropped. I didn't scream or cry, I was too frightened and hurt. Mama picked me up and we went back up the hill to grandmother's house. As we approached the house, I saw Daddy in the swing, overalls on, no shirt and smiling. I went from being frightened and hurt too being very angry. "She lied to me, My mother lied to me," I was thinking, but I realized at that moment that Mama wished he had really died in the fire.

Daddy's family didn't care for Mama. They thought she was too pretty and knew nothing about farming. Mama came from a small town twelve miles from my grandfather's plantation. She didn't want to live with them anymore than they wanted her to. She lived there when she and Daddy were first married and she hated it. Grandmother and her daughters didn't like anyone except Daddy, the youngest son of fifteen children. She spoiled him until he was rotten and no good.

Mama watched us very closely because these people were mean. She watched what we ate and drank. She taught us never to eat or drink after anyone at Grandma's house. When she first married Daddy, she had a nervous breakdown living there. Mama said Grandmother hired a root lady to make her crazy. She was so sick she couldn't take care of her baby (Toney). She felt as if things were crawling in her hair, and she pulled almost all of it out.

She wouldn't eat meat smoked by my grandparents in their smokehouse. Once it was smoked, it was stored there during the winter and summer. During the summer months, the skippers (worms) would get in the meat. Mama would not eat the meat or the beans and peas because they didn't wash the meat before cooking it.

Grandmother was old by this time, but continued to dominate her family. She had two of her oldest granddaughters living there to help out with the work. Grandma was mean to them, too, and they felt overworked, so they didn't care about clean food or anything else.

Daddy finally began to try to get help for Mama by carrying her from root doctor to root doctor, and she soon got better. Finally we moved in another house on the property. Tobacco was stored in one side and we lived in the other side. You could see the stars through the cracks in the wall and through the tin roof, There were cracks under the doors large enough for any snake with a mind to to come in.

I cried every night until I went to sleep because I was afraid. I begged Mama to let me sleep in the bed with her and Daddy. I told her that I saw monsters with big red eyes looking at me every time I poked my head out from under the covers. "Well, put the covers back over your head," Mama would say.

"Mama, p-l-e-a-s-e," I begged. "Mama, would you please make her shut up and go to sleep," Toney would say. My brother never really complained. I really think he tried very hard not to cause any kind of problem, because he was afraid, too.

Daddy never really worked. He had people farming for him to do his work. Grandmother would give him the money to pay his sharecroppers. He was mean and abusive to the people who worked for him, and he was mean and abusive to us. He would bring his women home with him. They waited in the car while he took his bath and changed his clothes. Mama dared not say a word to him because he would beat her down in front of them. We were all afraid of him.

One Saturday night, he was driving us home from town drunk, calling us all kinds of names, cursing and driving more than a hundred miles an hour. He slowed the car down and pushed Mama out. Toney and I were screaming and crying. We thought Mama was dead. We didn't know what happened to her. She had simply disappeared.

Daddy came home to Grandmother's house where he, Toney, and I now lived, made us get out of bed, carried us down the by the graveyard, and beat us as though we were adults, trying to make us tell where Mama was, but we didn't know; we thought she was dead.

Doll, one of my favorite cousins and her mother, Auntie Carrie, heard us screaming and crying, and they ran all the way down by the grave yard—a full half-mile—to make him stop. Doll had her shot gun. "Sun," she said to Daddy, "if you hit those kids again I will shoot you." Daddy jumped in the car and sped off.

We all walked back to Grandma's house. My face was all bruised, scratched and bleeding. My eyes were black. I had never been beaten that badly. Toney's, face was red. He was trying to hold back the tears in front of everyone. "We didn't do anything. We don't know where Mama is. I don't know why Daddy wants to treat us like this," Toney said.

"We haven't seen her since Daddy pushed her out the car," I added. Our clothes were torn, and we were cold and scared. Doll tended to our bruises and found something warm for us to put on. Toney and I looked at each other with very sad eyes without having to say a word. Each of us knew what the other was thinking. We were wondering, "What's going to happen to us." We had no place to go, no mother to care for us. She might or might not be alive. We had no daddy, because he didn't love us and wished that we were dead. I was crying, because my brother looked so sad, and he was trying to hold his tears back because he thought I looked so sad.

Just as we begin warming up in front of the fire place, we heard the sound of a car. The country is very quiet, especially at night. You can hear the sound of an automobile a mile away, traveling through the quietness of the woods. We looked out the window and saw the car lights. We were very scared. It was Daddy. He got out of the car and cursed everybody out, including Grandma. She tried to stand up to him, but she was too old. We all huddled in Grandma's room. Daddy walked in and out of the house all night, cursing and saying things about Mama, calling everyone all kinds of m——r f——s. We were his children, and he could beat our asses anytime he wanted to and anyone else that f——d with him, he shouted. By morning, though, he had fallen asleep.

Someone got word to Mama. I'm not sure who it was even now. She came back late one night and sneaked us out with the help of a couple of her friends. Mama took one look at me and couldn't stop crying. She fell on her knees and began to pray: "Dear God, help me Lord. We deserve more than this, Lord. More than having to run for our lives through the woods and hide because we are being shot at, kicked and beaten. Help me Lord. Lord, I have no skills, no mother and father. I need you, dear God. Help me find and make a home for my children." That night Mama became a strong woman, a woman like no other I know.

Chapter Three

I RECOGNIZED FROM AN early age that if something didn't happen to make us leave and stay gone, someone would eventually get killed. Toney was getting old enough to try to keep Daddy from beating and kicking Mama. Daddy's driving was getting faster and more reckless. He was boxing Toney around.

Mama was never a well person, but she almost never complained. I thought Daddy did everything he could to make her complain, so he would have an excuse to beat her. The beating just before the last beating that caused us to go away for good was frightening. Daddy had Mama down. I was screaming, crying for him to stop hurting her. Toney was screaming, too, but Daddy wouldn't let her up off the ground and wouldn't stop beating her. Toney picked up the hatchet, hit Daddy on the leg and broke it. Toney had saved her this time. With Daddy's leg in a cast, we didn't have to run away, and it would be a while before he could hurt us.

Daddy would often bring one of his drunk friends home with him, like Red. Red had peg legs. The story goes that he was drunk and went to sleep on a train track and the train ran over his legs. Daddy made Mama get out of bed at 2AM—time didn't matter with Daddy—to start a fire in the stove and cook for Red and him.

"Sun, man, just drop me off at home. I'm not hungry," Red said.

"Hell, man, you just told me you love the way Lucille cooks. Damn, let her get her ass up and cook. The bitch don't have nothing else to do. She'll do what I tell her," Daddy said. "You ain't going home. I ain't taking you home," Daddy told Red.

Mama asked to speak with him in the kitchen. "We don't have room for Red, as I have told you before," she said. "The kids and I washed all the quilts yesterday, and that's a very hard job. I don't want the kids having to sleep under the quilts after other people. If you don't mind, take Red home."

Mama, pleaded with Daddy but he only said, "Bitch, you don't tell me what to do! I said Red can stay. "

Mama went on anyway. "It's not easy drawing water from the well, boiling the quilts and scrubbing them on a wash board," she said.

"Bitch I told you to shut the f-k up, Daddy said, and he slapped her down and kicked her. Toney and I screamed, "Daddy please don't hurt Mama. "

"Shut the f-k up," he said. "This is my house. You will do what I tell you to do. I will bring home any m----r f---r I want to any time I want to. Now get your ass up and finish cooking. I mean now. "

Mama pulled herself up from the floor with help from Toney and me, as we all were crying silently. We were too afraid to cry aloud.

Daddy sat in front off the fire place with Red, laughing.

Red said "Man, don't treat them like that." Daddy was picking his teeth with a straw. I could tell he got angry when Red asked him not to treat us that way, because he jumped up out of his chair and threw the straw into the fire. "Shut your cripple ass up," he said, and laughed.

The three of us went into the kitchen, by lamp light, the only lights we had. Mama's face begin to swell. She used her hand to support her back, where he had kicked her. It was cold in the kitchen. Wind rushed in from cracks under the door, whistled in around the wooden windows. Mama pushed our black cat off the table and told Toney and me to lay our heads down on it and try to go to sleep to make sure we didn't get in Daddy's way. We couldn't go to bed, because the beds were in the room with the only fire place we had and Red and Daddy were sitting there.

We heard Daddy ask Red if he would like to have another beer. He went to the car to get his beer and snuff. Mama was finished cooking, and we tried to wait for a chance to run. The house was getting very cold again. All the wood had burned out and needed to be replaced.

"Toney, get up, go out and get some wood for the fire," Daddy said.

"Daddy, it's dark outside, and I'm scared".

"Your mama just making a sissy out of you. Get your little ass up and be a man. Get the f—g wood," Daddy said, and slapped Toney down as if he were hitting another man. I jumped on Daddy's leg and started biting him. He slapped me against the wall. Mama was screaming. We all were crying.

Red said, "Man, don't do this," but Daddy just shouted, "You little bastards, I'll kill all of you. He went for his gun. We ran out of the house and into woods in the cold, without our coats. Daddy shot three times through the woods. We lay flat on the ground until we didn't hear any more shooting. We made it to Auntie Carrie's house. We knew we would be safe there. Doll would stand up to Daddy if she had too.

Auntie Carrie made a fire to get us warm, and I went to sleep. Morning came, and so did Daddy. I thought, "Lord please don't let Mama go back there. It will only happen again next weekend and every weekend the rest of our lives. He's going to kill us one of these days. "

I knew Mama loved him or thought she did and felt that she couldn't do any better. I hated living always afraid.

Chapter Four

IT WAS SUMMER OF 1949, and the "rolling store" came around every Thursday, with candy, sodas, bottles of Kool-aid, Johnny Cakes and other goodies. Mama had only enough money to buy a ten-cent block of ice.

"Would you kids rather have milk shakes today with your tea cakes?" she asked. We never complained. We knew that it meant she had no money.

"A ten-cent block of ice please," Mama said to the rolling store man.

"Hook, would you help your brother make a fire in the stove? Tomorrow is his birthday, and I'm going to make a chocolate cake. When you finish with the fire, I'll have your milk shakes ready to cool you off," she said.

Toney and I wasted no time getting that stove going. Mama's milk shakes were the best. They were made from canned milk, vanilla flavoring, one egg, water and lots of sugar and ice. It didn't take much to make the three of us happy as long as we were together.

It was getting dark. Daddy hadn't been home since morning. We were all beginning to get nervous, not knowing what mood he was coming home in. Mama saw the dark mood fall over our faces. We pretended not to notice, but we saw it on her face first. She tried to lift our spirits.

"Tomorrow we are going to make ice cream," she said, "We will have ice cream and cake for your birthday, Toney."

Mama made ice cream straight from heaven, in a can that once had syrup in it. She mixed milk, eggs, flavoring and heaven knows what else together. Once this was done, she surrounded the bucket with ice, and we turned it from one side to the other until it was ready. The three of us always celebrated Toney's and my birthdays, even though Daddy was never there.

"It's time to wash up for bed," Mama said.

"I am not sleepy. Do I really have to wash, Mama?" said Toney.

"Of course you do; if you should get sick through the night and had to be hospitalized or go to the doctor, I think you would want to be clean," she said.

"Not me," I said. "If we get sick we couldn't go to the doctor anyway. Who's going to take us, and how would we pay for it?"

"Well! You both will take a bath anyway, whether you get sick or not," Mama said.

We all heard Daddy's car drive up at the same time. I could see the fear in Toney's face. I thought it was a good thing we didn't take a bath. We wouldn't have had time to finish before Daddy came home drunk. We never wanted to get caught in a position where we couldn't run if we had to. We often slept in our clothes just in case we had to run for our lives.

Daddy staggered through the door. "Get your asses up," he said. "I want these pork chops fried. "

"Fry them yourself," Mama answered.

"Oh God!" I thought. "Why did Mama say that? What's wrong with her? She must have some kind of death wish. "

"Bitch, you do what I tell you to do," Daddy said, and slapped her over.

Mama, screamed out, and so did Toney and I. He kicked her and punched her in the head. They fought until Mama's clothes were torn off. We were crying and begging Daddy not to hurt her.

"I'll cook whatever you want, just stop," Mama finally said. She was bloody.

"Lord, how much more of this can we take," I thought.

"OK, just let us go outside and get the wood to start a fire in the stove," Mama said, "Put your shoes on and come help me get the wood, both of you. Hurry, and get your coats," Mama said .

Once we got outside we ran in the woods to hide. We could hear Daddy calling. "I should have known you were go-ing to run, you m---r f---s," he shouted. He started looking for us in the car, shining the headlights into the woods.

"Lay down flat on the ground and don't move. He might see you," Mama said. We stayed in the woods the rest of the night. We heard him leave home around eight the next morn-ing to pick up his workers, and we came home. We knew Dad-dy wouldn't get drunk for the rest of the week. Mama wanted to leave him, but she felt that she had no place to go and no way to take care of us. Her mother had died one week before I was born and her father died shortly afterward.

Daddy returned after picking up the workers and taking them to their job sites. The car door slammed. We could hear him spitting from the snuff he used as he walked in. We were eating breakfast: smoked sausages, home made biscuits, home made syrup and fresh milk from our cow.

No one said anything for more than three minutes, when suddenly the kitchen door opened. I could tell Mama didn't know whether to continue eating breakfast with us or run. We each heard the beating of our hearts as we sat around our broken-down, three-legged, kitchen table. Our hands were shaking so bad I could hear the sound of our forks tapping the tin plates we were eating from.

"Why are you all so quiet," Daddy said? No one would say a word. I knew Daddy was harmless when he was sober.

"What would you say after someone beat you down like a dog?" I replied.

"Girl, I didn't hurt you all," he said .

"Then why did we have to run from you last night?" I asked. Mama never said a word, and neither did Toney. I am the only one that would speak up, but I certainly chose my times carefully.

Chapter Five

THE FOLLOWING DAY, TONEY and I returned home from school. Mama and Daddy weren't at home. I knew he had taken her into town to buy her something new and pretty. It always worked. "When will she learn?" I thought. "I am only nine years old and I can see through that. " I was getting tried of going to school facing the kids of my Daddy's women, knowing that my daddy and their mothers were seeing each other.

The school was right down the hill on Grandpa's, property, a one-room schoolhouse with a pot-bellied stove. The graveyard wasn't more than twenty feet behind the school. The older kids would keep the younger kids controlled by telling us that they would let us sink in the graves and no one would ever see us again.

Once a month the health department came to give shots for smallpox and other childhood diseases, and once a month the county gave the school a box of apples. The older kids would take the apples from the smaller ones by scaring them about the cemetery.

Mama started walking down the hill to meet us every day after school.

"Why do you walk Hook and Gruff from school everyday, Lou?" Daddy asked. "You ain't doing nothing. But making them no-count. Let the little bastards fend for themselves," he said.

"How do you know I meet them after school everyday? Mama asked.

"I know every m—r f——g thing that goes on," he said. I could tell Mama had hit a nerve; Daddy was getting angry. Mama, couldn't keep her mouth closed sometimes, and before Toney and I could move out the way they were fighting. Before Daddy had a chance to really beat Mama up, Mr. Stevens stopped by. He owned the farm next to Grandpa's. Mr. Stevens was white, and Daddy was and continues to be very afraid of whites. Mr. Stevens needed Daddy to help move his cotton from the truck to the barn. We were so happy that he came for Daddy. Daddy had already beaten Mama enough to tear her clothes off. The three of us hid so that Mr. Stevens couldn't see us, huddled together in the corner, crying.

"Mama, are you alright," I asked? I knew whatever work he was doing for Mr. Stevens, Daddy was going to get paid for, which meant he was going to be able to get drunk in the middle of the week, and I knew that spelled trouble for the three of us.

"Mama, why do we have to take this? Why don't we find away to kill him ?" I asked.

"Hook, don't ever let me hear you talk about killing someone. Killing is wrong," she said

"If we don't kill him, Mama, he's going to kill one of us. I hate him. I hate the way he treats us and especially the way he treats you. You deserve better."

"I promise, Baby, it's going to be alright," she said.

Mama heard the mailman pass. She jumped up and began throwing our clothes in a paper bag. "Hurry! Get yourselves together by the time the mail man comes back by," she said.

Mr. Almond, the mailman also used his car as a kind of country taxi cab. The rides were twenty-five cents, but Mr. Almond often would not take money from us. I thought, "Even Mr. Almond knows when we are on the run. I hate this life, I hate this. If I was old enough I would kill him all by myself. "

Mr. Almond dropped us off at the bus station, and we walked to the Silver Moon Café that her cousin Ed owned. He gave us enough money to catch the Trailways bus, and his wife made box lunches for us to eat as we travelled.

We moved to Cottonton, Alabama, with Mama's brother. There were too many people living in that house, and I realized we couldn't stay there long. The good thing about being there was that Daddy was afraid of Mama's brother. He was the only person in the world Daddy was afraid of besides white people. Daddy knew Uncle Newt had a reputation for a hot temper and for killing a man. However, he finally got up the nerve to come to Alabama. I don't know if Daddy was just good enough of a talker to talk Mama into coming home or Mama realized that we just weren't going to be able to stay there because it was so crowded.

Uncle Newt had a long talk with Daddy and told him if he ever hurt his sister again he would kill him. "I mean it, Sun, I will kill you," he said.

Well, everything went real good after we got home for almost a year. Then Uncle Newt died. After that, Daddy's old habits started up again and got progressively worse. Now there was no one Daddy was afraid of.

Chapter Six

It was December, 1953. Toney and I were playing on top of a sawdust pile, climbing to the top and sliding two stories down on a piece of cardboard box, racing to see who would get to the bottom first. It was beginning to rain, which made the saw dust smell fresh and new like boards for building a new house—such a pleasant smell I thought.

"Hook! Gruff!" Mama was calling. We saw her coming with a stick in her hand. "What are you all doing?" she asked when she saw us on the pile. Do you realize that you could sink down in the sawdust and die, never to be seen again? Get off there!"

We must have hesitated because Mama said, "Come here, and I mean now!" She told us to go in and change our clothes. We were going to Grandma's, she explained.

"I don't want to go there, Mama," I said. "Why can't I stay home until you come back? "

Mama gave me a look. "Because," she said.

"Because what?" I asked.

"Because your grandpa is dying. He's not going to make it through the night. I thought you all would like to see him before he dies. He stopped eating this week, and he doesn't open his eyes anymore. He's breathing deep and hard. He has a rattling sound in the throat," Mama said.

Grandpa, was a tall, very dark, one-armed, bald-headed man. Anyone could look at him and tell he was once a very handsome man. I was thinking, "I am really going to miss Grandpa. He believed in me. He thought that somehow God made a mistake and made me a girl instead of a boy and Toney should have been a girl."

Toney and I were called Gruff and Hook because of Grandpa. My hair was long and thick. Mama would plat it in a hundred small plats, and Grandpa didn't like it. He said it looked as though I had horns. So he started calling me Hook. Toney's head was hard like a Billy goat, Grandpa said, and he started calling him Gruff. Soon everyone was calling us by those names.

Grandpa thought Daddy was spoiled and sorry. He thought Mama deserved better, so he was very sensitive to the things we were going through with Daddy. Grandpa had to shoot at Daddy once for fighting him.

I walked around in a daze, always thinking, "I am dreaming. I will wake up soon."

Every Sunday after returning from church, where Grandpa never went unless someone very close in the family had died, even though he had given land and built the churches for the family and the share croppers, his attendance was poor. The churches—Baptist and Methodist—stood about five hundred yards apart. They had long bench seats made of planks with space between them. When I lay my head in Mama's lap to go to sleep I cold see everyone on the bench in the next row.

The church was hot in the summer and cold in the winter. There was red carpet only on the pulpit. The church had never been painted inside or outside, and there was no running water or electricity—only a well and outside toilets. Mama wouldn't let me go in the outhouse; she was afraid snakes would be hiding in there. The church had board shutters at the windows. If we were late getting to church we would peep through the window so we would know if it was the right time to go in.

Grandma would beat the hell out of us for peeping in the windows if she saw us. She would come out of the church, take you behind the church and try to kill you. It made church almost as depressing as home. For that reason I mostly went to the Methodist Church with Aunt Carrie, Doll and her sisters. They had a bell at that church, and I was allowed to ring it on Sundays.

I didn't like Mama to go to that Baptist Church, because she would always do the devotional, praying and crying. Daddy's women and their children went to that Church. Toney and I went so we could protect Mama. Grandpa would surely leave when Mama started to cry. He would take off his soft leather high top shoes, tie the strings together, throw them across his shoulders and walk a mile and a half home.

"Come on kids, let's go home and shake the money tree," Grandpa would say. He was referring to a hedge bush tree on the side of his house. I used to sneak and shake that tree, but there was nothing there. I couldn't understand how that tree only recognized Grandpa. Nothing ever fell for me. I decided to watch him very closely to see if he held the tree any special way this time. "Don't stand back there, Hook," Grandpa told me, "Come up closer so your chances of getting some money will be just as great as the other kids. "

I looked back at Mama, and she was smiling, almost laughing. "Go up closer, Honey," she said.

I was going to take my chances just to watch to see exactly how he was shaking the tree. Grandpa was smiling—almost a laugh also—and the grandkids were ready to scramble under the tree for the money, and so was I. I wanted to do both, watch and scramble, but scrambling for the money won. When Grandpa started shaking that tree, if everyone didn't find money on the ground, Grandpa would give us some from his pocket—only it might not be as much as you would pick up from the ground.

Grandpa is gone now. I will always miss him and remember him. After the funeral, Daddy drank and raised hell all week. His sisters and brothers just kept telling him, "Son, Pa is dead. Why can't you act right at least until we bury him.

"M—r f—r, don't tell me what to do," Daddy said.

Mama, Toney, and I stayed very quiet, and we were afraid, because we knew he didn't care who died when he got ready to beat us up and show off on us.

Chapter Seven

THE SCHOOL BUS PUT Toney and me off by the highway, and we walked up to the house. Mama was on the side of the house bent over the wash tub washing clothes. We ran over and gave her a big hug and kiss and went inside to change our school clothes. I fried some sweet potatoes for a sweet potato sandwich. Toney and I sat on the steps of the front porch in the sunshine so we could look at Mama and eat at the same time. We heard Mama scream. "Help, help. Somebody, please help, please help us. Get some water. I see smoke. The house is on fire, Hurry! Hurry! Hurry! "

Toney ran to the well and started drawing water from the well to pour on the fire, but it didn't work. The smoke and fire began to spread, burning rapidly on the side by the chimney. It was too far out of control for the three of us to do anything about it. The house was made of very old pine, the kind one would use for starting a fire because it contained so much resin.

Our house burned down to the ground once again. Mama fell to the ground crying. We were just standing there over Mama and crying too. I was thinking, "My heart is burning out once again. "

Daddy drove up. "What happened ? What happened?" Daddy yelled.

"It started burning around the chimney," Mama said.

"The house is old and so is the chimney," Daddy said. "It most likely had cracks in it and the sparks got through to the wood part."

Daddy showed no remorse. The only thing that really mattered to the three of us now was, where would we go from here. Once again we had to move into Grandma's house. Mama has always believed that somehow Daddy was responsible for the first shack that burned to get the insurance money. We lost everything once again, and it was almost Christmas. It really didn't seem to bother Daddy.

Three weeks had passed since Grandpa's death and the burning of our house, and Daddy was terrible. He was hostile to everyone living in Grandma's house including Grandma herself, and she was eighty-five years old.

Daddy was drinking every day now and keeping everyone up almost all night walking around and cursing everyone. It had not been any better for us. As a matter of fact it had gotten worst. All three of us had turned into a bag of nerves.

Mama moved Toney and me to Florida, where we lived for two months. That's where Mama had run off to when Toney and I had no idea where she was, after Daddy had pushed her out the moving car and we thought she was dead. She had landed her first job—a waitress in a sandwich shop. Mama thought she would be able to make enough money with tips to take care of the three of us. It didn't work. She had to pay room and board to an old couple who allowed us to rent one room and gave us the use of the bath room.

We were living in a little neighborhood in Jacksonville near a train yard by the river. We couldn't get to sleep because the trains were coming and going all day and all night. The river had an awful smell of sulphur and the drinking water had the same taste. Mama, Toney and I slept in the same bed. I hated it. I hated having to live like this. We walked around the corner twice a day to eat breakfast and dinner with Mama's niece and her family of five. Even though Mama helped pay for the food, we weren't getting enough to eat and it was just too much for Mama to do. It was too costly, and we were unhappy. Mama prayed all night every night and we all cried ourselves to sleep every night

I hated moving, and I still hate moving. As far back as I can remember, we were moving or running away from Daddy and returning after weeks and sometimes a month or two. At any rate, I would never allow myself to become too close or friendly with other kids because I didn't know how long we would be living in one place. It made me a very cold person, because I knew as well as Daddy knew that when he was ready, all he had to do was come and romance Mama, and she would go back to him and the process would start all over again. I felt as though we lived through hell.

Two months later Mama, Toney, and I moved back to Georgia. We lived with her sister, Auntie Mae, Auntie Mae's daughter, Vera, and Vera's baby girl, Ann. We all lived in a four room house. I could see this wasn't going to work, but what the heck, Mama would go back to Daddy anyway. Most of the time I just wanted to lay low, close my eyes and die. No one ever asked Toney and me what we wanted. We weren't even allowed to express our feelings or have an opinion. We had learned to deal with just about anything. Nothing could be any worse than what we had been through.

Mama got a job on the local air force base doing domestic work. She worked every day and sometimes baby-sat on Sundays. Vera had never been married—a married man fathered her daughter, Ann. I never knew his name, but he worked for a dairy. Every two days he would bring milk for the baby. I never heard anyone say he ever brought money, only milk.

Chapter Eight

DADDY FOUND OUT WHERE we were. Every weekend he showed up, drunk, of course, loud-mouthed and speeding his car around and around in circles, causing a scene. I was so embarrassed. The neighbors all came out laughing, with the kids asking, "Is that your Daddy? "

"Lord please make him stop coming around here," I prayed. "Please let Mama make up her mind if she's going back to him or not and if not, Lord, please make him stop coming around here."

Toney was fifteen by this time, three years older than me and feeling his oats. He talked Mama into letting him go live with Daddy after it really seemed as though she wasn't going back and because she was having a serious problem trying to take care of us. She only earned fifty cents an hour from 9:00 AM to 3:00 PM, which was $15 a week for three people. Things were cheap those days, but we surely needed more than that.

Mama and Vera would go out on Friday and Saturday nights dancing, leaving me too baby-sit with little cousin Ann. I slept so hard they would have a problem trying to get in once returning home from dancing. I could hear Mama's voice telling me, "Girl, if you don't get up and open this door and let us in, I am going too beat your ass when I get in."

I replied by telling Mama, "I have opened the door once already. How many times you want me too open it." Of course, that wasn't true, because she and Vera were still banging on the door and Vera was laughing and saying, "Girl, get your crazy self up and open this door." Vera thought it was so funny that I walked in my sleep, used the bathroom in anyone's shoe, then would get back in bed without letting them in.

I became thirteen and started baby sitting for some of the people Mama worked for. I was getting a little happier now, because maybe we weren't going back to the country where everyone knew us and knew how Daddy treated us.

Mama and Vera started dating. I watched her face light up from having someone to treat her like a woman and a person. She began taking an interest in how she looked. She even bought some material for fifty cents a yard and sewed herself some skirts. After being away from Daddy for months, I began to relax even more. We had never been away that long. The day Mama came home and said, "You and I will be living two doors down the block in a room that has one large bed and a twin bed, I was happy because I realized we weren't going back and we didn't have to sleep together.

Two months after Toney had returned home with Daddy, they had a serious car wreck. The car flipped over three times, but their lives were spared. Mama was in an uproar. In addition, a year after he had been back with Daddy, Toney had gotten a girl pregnant. Mama was devastated.

I wanted to say, "Mama, I know the only reason Toney wanted too live with Daddy was so he could screw every farm girl on the property, just like his daddy." Hell, I knew that and

I was thirteen. But did any body ask me? No. Everyone tried to whisper around me about the fact that he wanted to live with Daddy. Now they were trying too hide the fact from me that he made a young farm hand pregnant. Why should I let Mama know that I knew when we had enough problems and I was trying too carve out a life for myself, little by little.

I noticed the boy who lived next door to me. The first time I laid eyes on him, I knew he was going to be my husband and the father of my children. I didn't know how, but I knew in my mind that it was going to happen, just as I knew my family called me Hook.

Chapter Nine

THE FIRST CHRISTMAS ON our own, I never expected
to get anything. I never did with Daddy other than a cardboard box of mixed nuts. I began to feel the usual holiday de-
pression come over me. Only Mama seemed to have a smile
on her face every day. I wasn't going to change her mood for
the holidays.

Three days before Christmas I was feeling even more depressed. Mama couldn't afford a Christmas tree, and we had
no place to bake cakes or any Christmas treats. As I walked
through the village I could smell cakes and hams being cooked.
Christmas trees were lighting up and my friend's mother asked
me if we were finished shopping.

"Yes, Ma'am," I replied, and ran home with tears in my
eyes.

I was trying to hide the tears from Mama, when she open
the door, smiling. I screamed. We had a tree, with lights and
presents. It was our first. I was so happy. John, Mama's friend,
God bless him, surprised us.

"You can't open your gifts until Christmas, "Mama said.

"I won't" Mama .

"I know you, Hook," Mama said, with a smile.

"OK, I won't open them."

John and Mama were laughing. Mama was happy because

they were able to make me happy. After John left, Mama and I sat there for hours just looking at the Christmas tree and the lights on the tree blinking on and off. With Mama's arms around me I was wondering if Mama was feeling as warm and as safe as I was, not having too be afraid that as the sun went down Daddy would come home and run us away.

When we were growing up Mama used to entertain us at night by sitting in the moonlight listening to the sounds of the owls and the partridge birds. We tried to mimic the sounds of the different animals until the night became still and we became afraid. Once inside Mama continued too entertain us by telling us stories that her parents once told her.

If we could manage to get the old newspapers from Grandma, once she finished reading them once or twice a month, Mama would use our entertainment time too make paste with flour and water and use the newspaper as wall paper to cover the cracks in the walls to keep the wind and cold out.

I hated having to live like animals. I hated it! Mama leaned over and kissed me on the cheek and said that things were going to be fine. I put my head in her lap and went to sleep watching my first beautiful Christmas tree.

Chapter Ten

THE LAST TIME DADDY showed up in Georgia, raising hell, trying to bulldoze his way in Auntie Mae's house, she got so and angry she picked him up and threw him off of her porch. Being the coward of a man that he was, he got up, dusted himself off, and left. I hoped he would never come back. "Who needs a man for a daddy that beats his wife and children," I thought.

After that incident Daddy came around about once a month, still drinking, but making a lot less noise. Eventually, I learned to think of my father as being dead. It worked for me. He wasn't doing anything to make life better for any of us. He didn't care how we were eating or living. When I would ask him for money, his response was "I don't have no damn money." I could hear the change in his pockets and watch him buy alcohol for anyone in the village that was crazy enough to ride in the car with him. I only wanted him to go away and stop making us ashamed. I started to hate him more and more. Sometimes when he would come around from the country, he wouldn't even talk to us but talk *at* us through his cursing. I couldn't believe my eyes and ears.

But this time, Mama walked out to Daddy's car with her hand on her hip, shaking her finger in his face. "C. H.,"— short for Charlie Henry—"you are welcome to come visit with the kids without the abusive language and the use of alcohol. Otherwise, I will have no choice but to call the police. "

That's when I knew Mama was no longer in love with Daddy, and that we were free, thanks be to God. When Mama came back in, I wanted to hug and kiss her for finally being able to stand on her own, where she paid rent, bought food, and gave her orders, but I couldn't because I wasn't supposed to know that she threatened to put Daddy in jail. Mama always instilled in us the idea that, no matter what, he was our daddy. I wish someone had reminded *him* that he was our daddy.

After he was long gone back to the country I could feel this sadness come over me, feeling sorry for him and us because we couldn't be a family. As awful as life was for us in the country, I loved that plantation. It was a part of my soul. It made me feel important when someone would say. "Those are Aunt Mae's and Uncle Charlie's grands." Everyone knew they were the most well-to-do blacks around, even though Mama, Toney, and I, in those years, lived a nightmare every weekend and sometimes through the week.

Later, during my first year in college, Mama told me that Daddy's niece and her family had moved from Africa and her husband was employed by the college. It made me feel wonderful. I now had a cousin from Daddy's family living in the same town. It made me feel as through I now had a sense of background and family. I really didn't remember her, and she was almost twenty years older than I was.

If you are related to daddy's family, your face will reveal it.

I saw my cousin crossing the campus one day. I was sure that I recognized her. She possessed all the family features. I was so happy and proud to have a cousin married to a professor, and owning a home near the college. It suddenly gave me a sense of pride. Well, that bubble was short-lived.

I ran over to her and said Hello. I explained who I was and that Mama had told me she had moved to the low country. She looked shocked. She looked me up and down and replied, "Oh. Hi. How are you?" And she walked away very fast, as through she were ashamed of me and didn't want anyone to see her talking to me.

I was hurt. She acted as though I didn't matter or maybe she was afraid to get friendly, fearing I might want or need something from her. I only wanted to be a relative, I thought to myself. I'm the one who should be ashamed—ashamed of her.

Chapter Eleven

AUNTIE M., THE SECOND oldest child of my grandparents, was a very vibrant person at one time but had fallen very ill with rheumatoid arthritis. The story goes that she was such a bad person, God had paralyzed her. Her hands and fingers were as stiff as if she were getting ready to use her hands to karate chop someone. She could only raise her arm and hands to reach her nose. She couldn't wash her own face. She slept in a sitting position because her legs would not straighten out. Someone would have to pick her up from behind, under her arms, and someone would have to pick her stiff legs up from the front to put her on the slop jar or give her a bath.

Mama thought she had T. B., and she didn't want us around her She always seemed to have a cold deep down in the throat Mama had Toney and me paralyzed with fear about eating or drinking anything at Grandma's house, which was hard for us to avoid. Many times when Daddy would run Mama away, we had to stay there.

Auntie M. was mean. If we didn't wait on her hand and foot, or hurry back when she asked us to do something, she would beat us. Just because Auntie M. couldn't walk we were afraid of her. Grandma raised a borderline mentally retarded man whose name was Hill. Auntie M. would have him run us down, back our butts up to Auntie M. and she would stick straight pins in us to control us. The last time Auntie M. had Hill to chase me down, I cursed both of them out. No damn body was going to stick any more damn pins in by butt. I told Auntie M. that Mama said those pins are poison, and she could just stick them in her own, mean, crippled ass. "Don't put your damn hands on me ever again," I said.

Toney never said a word. I said "Toney, we don't have to stay over here. Let's go home to our own house and wait for Mama and Daddy. I will not let a cripple woman hurt me anymore. "

We went home. I knew Toney would not speak up for himself, and I was not going to let them hurt him like they did me. Auntie M. hated Mama and Mama's children. She loved Daddy. She would give him money, lie for him, steal for him, and use Hill to help steal money from Grandma for him. She paid Hill with snuff she would buy for him from the Rolling Store.

Daddy didn't discriminate when he was drinking. Everybody was in for it. If he needed money and Auntie M. refused, Daddy would slap her around, too. He would take the money she had pinned under her smelly dress and leave. I wondered how Mama could have married into a family that was so mean both to her and to each other. Mama read my mind.

"Your Daddy wasn't always like this," Mama said.

"He was once a nice person. Didn't use alcohol or run around on me. He changed, he just changed. I don't know what happened. He turned into a monster—with his mother's help. "

"Why do you say with Grandma's help?" Mama.

"Because she spoiled him. Your grandmother gave him everything he wanted as long as he was there for her. He's your grandma's baby," Mama said.

Grandma and Daddy carried Auntie M. to every root doctor they could find between South Carolina and Georgia, trying to make her walk. They traveled late at night because Daddy was afraid of white people and didn't want to travel during the day. He was afraid the law would stop him in the small towns and put him in jail because he had a nice car. Daddy would only allow us to play the car radio before we reached the town limits. He would cut the radio off until we got through any town. Daddy knew he had power only over the plantation and over Mama, Toney and me.

"They are such damn crazy fools," Mama would say. "Anyone can see that as stiff and as long as your Auntie M.'s bones have been like that, it would be hard for Jesus himself to make her walk.

Nevertheless the three of us, our pillows, quilts, and a bucket to use the bathroom in, traveled along with Daddy and Auntie M. Mama would make food for us to eat, because Daddy would only stop for gas. Besides, three were no places for blacks to stop to eat as we traveled.

The first few times Daddy carried Auntie M. to a root doctor, I kept watching her, waiting for her to start walking.

"Mama, when will Auntie M. start walking?" I asked.

Mama looked at me and couldn't stop laughing.

"What's wrong Mama?"

"Nothing is wrong, Honey," Mama said.

"Why are you laughing? What's so funny?" I asked Mama.

"You are, Honey." Mama continued to laugh, stopping long enough to say that Auntie M. would walk when hell froze over. Auntie M. died in 1970, still bent double with arthritis.

One day, Mrs. Emma, from Savannah, told Daddy there was money and oil on the land that had been buried by slaves. Daddy dug up most of Grandpa's farm, leaving big holes all over the place, looking for money or oil wherever Mrs. Emma pointed her finger. Mama's joy was laughing at Daddy and his family behind their backs.

Mama said, "All of them are crazy as hell. "

"Hook, Gruff," Mama would say to us. "Don't play too far from home. You may fall in one of those money holes your Daddy has dug."

Mama laughed so much that pretty soon it was funny to Toney and me, too, It was also fun, because we got to travel a little. Daddy would never use alcohol when he was dealing with root doctors, which made it fun for Mama, Toney and me.

Daddy would buy two or three car batteries at one time because he used the lights on his truck to see how and where to dig in the middle of the night.

"Damn Fool," Mama said. "God has already given him gold and oil and he's too damn stupid to realize it."

I thought to myself, "Do other people live this way? Are we different? Is this what it will be like as a grown up?"

Chapter Twelve

LIFE WAS SLOWLY IMPROVING for the three of us. Toney was seventeen years old and had finished high school. He came once again to live with Mama and me, which meant we needed a larger place to live. We continued to be in bad need of money. I don't know how Mama managed to take care of Toney living with Daddy and me living with her on a domestic's pay.

I had just begun high school. I was able to do enough baby sitting too buy myself a few school clothes. Toney was working as a bag boy at the super market, making very good tips. Soon with his tips and money Mama managed to save, he bought his first car, a 1954, light peach, two door, hard top Ford, with one door peach and the other door brown. But he was so proud of it and washed it all the time.

I knew in my heart we were never going back to live with Daddy, and Daddy knew it too. He was hardly ever around. We were all happy about that because it seemed as if we were as normal as anyone else living in the village.

I could see Mama's strength had grown. She, Cousin Ann, and twelve of their friends organized a social club for Ladies (The Golden Locket Social Club) which lasted for thirty-five years. They raised money by giving bus rides to different beaches, selling dinners, having dances at the Ruby Two Spot

Club and the V. F. W. Club.

Mama began to really enjoy being alive, though John would never go out dancing or in public places with Mama. He mostly came around when I was in school. I found out that there was a reason for that. John was married. Mama begin too lose interest in John, even though he was a good man. She knew that the relationship was a dead end street.

The Air Force Base was closing, which meant she wouldn't have a job, and I couldn't babysit anymore. She only allowed me to babysit for the same people she worked for doing the day—three different families. She wasn't going to trust anyone she didn't know.

Every Saturday night the Golden Locket Ladies went out dancing with their husbands, those that had husbands. All the night clubs closed at 12:30, and there was no place for them to go.

Mama never used alcohol, she only used her mind, she said. She said that smart people sell alcohol and fools buy it Mama had the bright idea of using our house for a restaurant for special friends and their own special friends. She would not let you in if she didn't know who you were or if one of her friends didn't know you very well.

I wasn't allowed out of my bedroom on these occasions, but I would listen to them tell jokes and laugh as Mama would sell them the best potato salad in the world with fried fish or chicken. Soon it was no longer just Saturday night she cooked, but Thursday, Friday, and Saturday. And it was paying off, which was good, because we needed an income.

Mama asked Toney how he felt about her selling alcohol to her friends. They would never ask me about such matters, but I was always listening and thinking.

Moonshine was mostly the choice of alcohol for poor blacks at that time. Mama and Toney made two of the best business people I knew. Toney started hauling the unlawful product and Mama started selling it. The money was very good. Mama begin running week-long accounts on food and drinks for special people. They would always pay on Friday or Saturday.

Mama ran a good, strict business. "You can drink and socialize, but there will be no drunkenness or strong language in my house," Mama said. "If you think you can't follow the rules, then you can't come in." Sometimes she would give them written rules before they were served if that was their first time. .

Mama's best friend Lillie Mae lived across the street. Lillie Mae was very large, strong, cheerful lady. She never left Mama alone on the weekend.

I called her "Fat, the bouncer. " She would laugh. She thought that was so funny.

"Lucille, I am going to make sure you all are alright," Fat said. "Nobody's going to bother *me*." And she laughed.

Mama paid Lillie Mae for helping her cook and serve on the weekends, even though Fat was getting lots of free food and drinks from everyone. I never saw Mama dating anymore. I was beginning to worry about her because her health was failing.

Lillie Mae introduced Mama to her cousin William. He was a handsome man, with curly hair, thin, and brown skinned, a man with a brown hat cocked to one side. "I know him," I thought to myself. "My friend and I use to see him in the Village. We thought he was so cute when he would pass us in his car."

"Hello! My name is William Reddick," he introduced himself. "Nice to finally meet you."

"Thanks. It's nice to meet you," Mama replied.

Fat laughed. "Cut out the formal shit, guys. I want some food and give us a half pint," she said.

I was peeping through my key hole and watching William watching Mama. I soon realized that Mama was watching him, too. I no longer thought he was cute, now that I knew they were interested in each other. It seemed to me that he talked too much, drank too much, and smoked too much.

William worked at a bakery shop as a baker. I did enjoy the donuts he brought every day and so did Mama and Toney.

I could see the excitement in her eyes. "Why aren't you a merchant seaman now," I asked.

He smiled. "The army needed me," he replied.

"What kind of work did you do on the ship, I asked.

"I was a cook," he said.

"Why don't you stop asking so many questions, Hook?" Mama said.

But William said he didn't mind my questions. "I am planning to go back to work on the ship just as soon as they will take me back, young lady," William said.

Chapter Thirteen

IN THE FALL OF 1960, Mama bought her first house—a small four-room house with and outside toilet—for three thousands dollars. I could feel and see the progress we were making. The three of us celebrated every milestone we made with prayer. Mama had great plans for all of us. She planned to buy more and more houses to rent out, but things didn't go the way she planned.

Toney got married in 1961, which meant they were no longer working as a team. Toney had to work for his wife and ready-made family. Mama was very depressed. She felt Toney's wife was looking for help, not a husband, and she was right.

Then, in 1962, I got married to the boy of my dreams—my first boyfriend, the boy I knew was going to be my husband, from the early age of twelve or thirteen, the boy next door,

Mama lived alone now. We lived on the other side of town in the project, but I visited her every day most of the time. Mama felt that I had a good husband and if anything happened to her I wouldn't be alone. She became a diabetic, and I worried about her.

Mama began to see William regularly.

I often wondered if she never dated anyone seriously because she felt she had responsibilities to raise me. That made me feel very sad, because so much of her life had been spent trying to take care of her children.

In November, the day before Thanksgiving, the ringing of the phone awakened me.

"Hook, I am so happy," Mama said.

William has received a notice from his old job. He will go back to being a cook on the ship. When he returns in six months we are getting married," she said. I could hear the joy in her voice.

"Mama, that's wonderful. I am happy for you," I told her.

"Are you really, Baby? "

"Mama, I think you should. If it doesn't turn out right, you are independent enough now. You don't have to put up with anything you don't like."

"Oh. , Baby, don't worry. I know this is right," she said.

I was happy and sad at the same time. The sadness came from remembering what Mama had gone through with Daddy, being a little afraid and hoping she never had to go through that again. Yet, I was very happy for her.

Toney and I arrived at Mama's house at the same time. We hugged her and begin horsing around with each other as we usually do. I heard something fall behind the sofa as we were horsing around. I reached back picked it up. It was a brown bag with what I though was a silver cap pistol in it. I put the gun to Toney's head and pulled the trigger. Toney moved his head slightly as I pulled the trigger. The gun went off. I dropped the gun. Toney fell to the floor, and Mama was screaming, "Oh, God. My child, my child. "

I was frozen to the spot, unable to move. Mama fell on her

knees besides what we thought was Toney's dead body. The sound from the gun made Toney deaf and too frightened to move. He thought he had been shot, and we thought he was dead

Finally Toney moved. Mama couldn't stop hugging him. "Thank you Jesus. Thank you Jesus. Oh. Thank you Jesus," she kept repeating as she sat on the floor with his head in her arms, crying.

I was still standing stiff in the same spot when William said, "G'anna, are you alright? "

I was unable to answer. William, begin shaking me. I could hear him talking, as if he were in the far distance.

"Are you alright?"

"Yes," I answered finally, and I begin to cry. "I'm sorry, I'm sorry. I didn't think it was real."

I couldn't stop crying and shaking. Finally, Toney was able to get off the floor. He came to me and hugged me.

"It's alright, I know you didn't do it on purpose. Come on stop crying."

And we hugged and cried together. I never remembered Mama ever consoling me. She kept repeating, "Thank you Jesus. My child, my child. "

It was William's gun. He walked to work at the bakery every morning at 4:00. The gun was his protection.

Thanksgiving was very special at Mama's house, the next day. I realized it could have very easily gone the other way. After the holidays, William began his merchant sea duties aboard on an oil tanker docked and leaving from New Orleans. William was happy he had a better-paying job, and Mama was happy that they would soon be married. She was like a teenager, dating for the first time. It was wonderful to see her this way. William would call her at every port of call. She couldn't wait to share the conversations with Vera and me everyday.

Three months later, Mama and Lillie Mae were watching the evening news and heard that a tanker had had an accident in New Orleans. A tanker was burning, men on fire were jumping overboard and there were deaths, no one knew how many. It turned out to be William's ship.

Lillie Mae called. "G'anna, can you come over to Lucille's for a minute?"

I knew Mama was a diabetic, I was thinking she must have passed out.

"Lillie Mae, is Mama alright?"

"Yes and no," Lillie Mae said. "She thinks William's ship has had an accident in New Orleans."

Before I could get there, William's brother Bill was there. He had seen the story on the evening news also. We made some telephone calls, but they weren't giving out any information. Days went by. All we knew was that a number of men were missing and a number were dead.

One week later Bill and Mama located William in a New Orleans hospital. After being slightly burned and overcome by smoke, he had been rescued. He had crawled up from the ship's dining room, through the black smoke , and onto the deck.

After recovering at the hospital, the company paid for him

to fly home. William never quite seemed the same. He didn't talk as much anymore and suffered severe headaches.

Nevertheless, Mama and William brought a home and got married in December of 1974. William's headaches were getting worst, and he began to lose that bubbly, talkative spirit. Mama insisted that he see a doctor, and finally he did.

The doctor sent him immediately to the V. A. hospital in Maryland. William called Mama. I was walking through the door, and he asked to speak to me. "G'anna," he said, "the doctors told me that I have lung cancer. " And he began to cry.

I was nearly speechless. "What do you mean. They told you that you have what? I didn't know how to respond to what he was saying, and I begin to cry, too. "Everything's going to be alright," I said.

I looked over at Mama. She was shaking her head in answer to my response.

"Mama and I are coming up to see you on the weekend. Please don't cry. I love you," I said, and I passed the phone back to Mama.

Daddy taught Toney and me to drive at the ages of twelve or thirteen, but I had never driven to or in a large city before. I was afraid, but I didn't want Mama to know it. Plus, I had no idea where to find the hospital upon arriving in Maryland.

"I can handle Maryland," I told myself.

We arrived at John Hopkins hospital on a Friday. This was my first experience watching someone very ill wither in such a short time. It was heart breaking.

We knew nothing about Maryland, and I asked the nurse where we could find the nearest and safest place for Mama to live during Willam's recovery. The nurse knew he wasn't going to get better, but I could tell she wasn't sure if we knew.

"I live with my aunt, and she has plenty of room. I will ask her if she'll rent your mother a room," the nurse said. I talk to my aunt every night about Mr. Redden. He is such a good patient. He talks about you all day," Mrs. Redden.

They were very nice. They lived very close to the hospital and never charged Mama for the two months she lived there.

When John Hopkins had done everything they could do for William, they sent him home. In October 1975, he died.

The next few months I watched Mama retreat into seclusion. I didn't know what to do. Mama kept telling me that she was alright, but I could see that she wasn't.

Mama had gotten used to spending all of her time with William, and they were very happy. William treated Mama as if they were always on a date, taking her to the movies, going to dinner, going out dancing. They were happy and enjoyed the company of each other.

"Mama, Bud and I would like to take you out to dinner and a movie," I would tell her.

"What kind of movie?" she would ask, as if it mattered. I knew she wasn't going.

"The name of the movie, Mama, is *The Ship that Fell From Grace With the Sea*," I replied. "You told me that you would like to see that movie. "

"No thank you, Honey. Maybe the next time," she said.

"We'll pick you up after the movie, to spend the night with G'anna and me," Bud said.

"No thanks. I'll stay at my own house. I got to get used to it at some point. I might as well begin now," she answered.

"Mama, I am really concerned about you. I don't want you to feel as if you are all alone, because you are not. I will stay with you," I said. I knew Mama was feeling all the things she had dealt with in her life time and feeling sorry for herself. She was trying to be strong, but it truly wasn't working. She was in pain, and Bud and I didn't know what to do.

"I want to be for her what she was for me when I was a child," I said to Bud.

I felt as though I were dying with her and having a nightmare at the same time about all the hard times and joyful times we had shared.

Chapter Fourteen

IT WAS BITTER COLD, and the ground was frozen hard. Toney and I walked a mile and a half every morning to get Old Daisy (the mule), from the barn at Grandma's house. When the harvest season was over, Daddy would plow the fields to turn over what was left from the harvest to fertilize the soil for the planting season.

Our hands and toes seemed frozen. Auntie M., lying in her bed next to the window with a view of everything within a mile would have Hill call Toney and me in to warm our hands and feet before we began on our trip home on Old Daisy.

I was afraid to ride on Old Daisy, but had no choice. Old Daisy was afraid to walk across the bridge, so we had to cross the creek to get home. Toney would try to force the mule across with us on his back by using his heel to poke him in the side. Daisy would back up until I almost slid off his rear end. I held Toney tightly around his waist to keep myself from screaming. I knew if I screamed Daisy would throw me off. Time was passing and we still had to walk miles to catch the school bus, because the school was no longer down the hill from where we lived.

We knew Daisy wasn't going to cross the bridge even through Toney tried to force her across every morning. "Stop kicking her Toney, you'll make her throw us off," I said.

"Shut up and hold on. I'm trying too keep from riding her through the creek. If we fall off we'll drown," Toney said.

Every morning brought this frightening experience. Most times Daisy stood there unused by Daddy all day after Toney and I had gone through all that trouble. Mama dared not say a thing, although she thought we were too young to have such responsibilities as he lay sleeping in bed.

The school bus arrived 7 AM. If we weren't standing by the side of the road the bus didn't bother to stop. "Hurry! Warm your hands and feet," Mama said. "The bus will be here soon."

We rushed to eat breakfast and drink the hot chocolate Mama always had waiting after the long trip too get Old Daisy. "I hear the bus coming up the hill," she said. We grabbed our books and ran out the door.

"Wait!" Mama said, "you are leaving your lunches."

I wanted the bus to leave us. It was cold, and the school was always freezing when we got there. The kids arrived before the teachers, made a fire in the pot-bellied stoves in the four classrooms, and waited for the rooms to get warm.

Chapter Fifteen

THE BOY NEXT DOOR finally noticed me. I was fourteen at that time, and he was older. Late one hot summer afternoon, I was sitting on the porch with the neighborhood kids, playing cards. The boy next door walked over and watched us play.

Around eight o'clock, all the kids went home. The boy invited himself to sit in the chair on the porch.

"Sit right here. " he said, indicating his lap. Blushing, I sat there. Before I could park my butt down my mother exclaimed, "I dare you. Go home! I don't want you around my daughter. You are too old," she said. "It is not polite to sit in a man's lap. That's the beginning of other things," Mama told me.

What other things? I wondered. What in the world was she talking about?. Why do older people say so many things you can't understand? Is it because you aren't allowed to question them? They never talked so you could understand the meaning of what they were trying to say.

I went into the one room that we were renting from a single woman, lay in my bed with the lights off ,and watched the boy next door in his kitchen from my window, dreaming about him being my husband and the father of my children.

I figured it would never happen. I was only fourteen-and-a-half years old. He was in college. Why would he have any thoughts about me? Mama would make sure they were only thoughts. She watched me like a hawk.

Summer was approaching, school was on break, and I had heard that he was going off on one of those jobs connected with the college. I didn't know when, because I wasn't allowed too talk to him. From my bed I watched through his kitchen window as though it were a job. Mama thought I was just following her orders, staying in our room all day during her working hours. She was happy about that because she didn't want me hanging around the single lady we rented from, either.

"She drinks too much and has too many men hanging around," Mama told me.

One morning at 6:00 AM I watched the bus pull up for the boy next door. "My summer is over," I thought. "I don't know where he's going. I can't watch him through the window anymore."

I wasn't at peace until I found out where he was. "He's at the Jolly Green Giant pea company," a friend told me. She was his cousin.

"Jolly Green Giant? Where is that?" I asked.

"Somewhere in Minnesota," she answered.

I couldn't imagine why he would go so far away to work. As summer came closer to an end, I begin worrying, not about the boy next door or about Mama going back to Daddy. I didn't have that worry about that any more. Too much time had gone by. Mama was independent now.

No, I was worried about high school! I was going to a new school in September, and I was afraid. How should I dress? I would need new clothes? I couldn't afford new clothes. Would it be easy for me to make friends? Would I get lost?

All of these fears and no one too share them with. I didn't want to worry Mama, with such stuff.

"Lord, help me with this new transition," I prayed.

The girls were very pretty, my friend told me. Was I going too look "country?" Would the kids like me?

I worried the summer away. I wondered if the kids would laugh if my mother went too school with me on my first day. "Mama can't afford too take a day off for you, crazy girl. You can handle this. So what if no one likes you? So what if your clothes aren't as pretty?"

"So what?" I thought.

Chapter Sixteen

MAMA HAD BEEN IN and out of the hospital following William's death. All the life and energy seemed to have disappeared. Toney and I noticed this, but Mama didn't admit to it. We didn't know what to do. She told us we don't need her anymore. "You have your own lives now. My job is complete," she said. It was almost as if she had nothing to live for and wanted to die. It made me very sad.

On July 12, 1991, Mama died. This was the saddest day of my life. At four in the morning, Mama called to tell me that she was getting ready to drive herself to the hospital.

"Drive yourself?" I exclaimed. "Wait just wait one minute. I'll be right there." Twenty minutes later we were arriving at the hospital.

"What seems too be wrong, Mama?" I asked.

"I am bleeding from my rectum," she said.

"Are you in pain? What happened to make you realize that you had blood in your stool?" I asked.

"The pain, the pain in my side," she said. "My side hurts so bad."

It seemed that Mama lay on the cold table at the hospital forever waiting for attention. Toney arrived. I went home to put on proper clothing. Mama was put in a room with all kinds of IVs. She continued to be in great pain. Surgery came.

A grapefruit-sized tumor was removed. The doctor said she had a fifty-fifty chance to live. I thought a fifty-fifty chance was very good and so did Toney until things begin to go wrong. The doctor needed to go back in for more surgery. The nurses said, "Fifty-fifty means there's a great chance she will die, and her chances of ever coming out of this are very slim. Let her be. Don't let the doctors cut her any more," the nurses said.

We didn't know what to do. The nurses were telling us not to do it. The doctors continued to say a fifty-fifty chance. We wanted to give Mama every chance to survive. "What if we said no to the doctors," Toney said, and later they find there was something that could have been done?"

Mama was on the respirator. We explained everything to her that they had explained to us. "Mama, squeeze my hand if you understand what I am saying," Toney said. One single tear would drop from her eye every time they would allow us in I. C. U. to visit her.

One and a half months went by and I never left her side. They couldn't stop the bleeding. She died at nine o'clock on a Friday night. It was the saddest day of my life.

Walking down the long corridors and out of the hospital holding Toney's hand, it seemed as if suddenly we were six and nine years old again. Only this time we were homeless. Without a mother. Lost. Just the two of us left in this big world alone, stumbling our way along in the dark.

There were arrangements to be made, so I couldn't let myself be overcome by grief. All the family and friends would come. I didn't want to see them. "This is Toney's and my private business," I told myself. I didn't want to hear people say they were sorry and what a good and wonderful person Mama was. I knew that already. All I wanted to do was die with Mama.

What about Mama's things? Her house, her clothes. I couldn't give them away. Who could wear five-and-a-half shoes? No one I knew.

"Oh-o-o God, why did you do this too us ?" I cried out. Why did you take my mama from us?" Mama always said that Jesus makes no mistakes, but he had made one this time. I thought I would never pray again.

My daughter visited at the hospital. She's a doctor.and understands death and dying. While she was there, she told me that she was going to have a baby. I should have been happy for her, but I didn't have the energy to be happy. Mama was dying. Couldn't she understand I couldn't let joy in, couldn't let anything in.

Still, I answered. "I think that's nice, Baby. How far along are you?"

"Two months, Mom," she said.

In the midst of all the sadness, Mama's voice crept inn. "Remember, every time a life goes out one will come in. My grandchild will be my replacement."

Chapter Seventeen

DADDY WAS SEVENTY-FIVE YEARS old when Mama died. He came to the funeral with one of his nephews, drinking alcohol. I could see all of his old ways trying to come out in front of everyone. He walked out to his car, started back into the house with a drink in his hand. I stepped in front of the door. "Not in here you won't drink. I'm sorry, but this is Mama's day, and there will be no drinking in this house," I said quietly so the others would not hear. Nothing was going to interfere with Mama's last day.

I never knew Mama knew so many people. The funeral line was two miles long. Her friends all told wonderful, sweet things and stories about her. There were so many of them. It was like a weight was lifted from me. I had thought that Mama passed this way with so few friends. How wrong I was! She had lived a wonderful life that I knew nothing about. After all, I had been married and living on my own for twenty-nine years. How could I possibly know how many people she knew?

I realized Mama had had a great life. It relieved me of some of the pain. "Thank you God," I thought. I felt as I did as a child, when Mama would allow me to take my shoes off and walk in the sand for the summer, feeling the sand sliding between my toes. I couldn't hold on to it, but yet it was there.

Thank you, friends of Mama.

Chapter Eighteen

PLAYING THE NUMBERS GAME was a big thing for Mama and Daddy. Mama sold her chicken eggs and used the money to play this game of chance. She was very good at the game right up until the day she died.

Every Friday night after Daddy left for his good times, Mama would gather Auntie Carrie's kids, Toney and me with a flash light and walk two miles through the darkness to play the numbers.

It was so much fun. Mama was a great story teller, and on these nights she told us ghost stories. "Remember not to drag behind," she would say. "The moon is shining bright and all the ghosts without heads are out tonight."

"Mama, please don't scare me," I would say.

"I'm not trying too scare you, Honey, but it's true," she said.

"Have you ever seen a ghost," Mama?

"I see them all the time," she said. "Especially when the moon is shining bright."

"What does it look like, Mama?"

"It looks human, sometimes. Once I saw a man without a head. I tried to outrun it, and it changed into a dog," Mama said.

"A dog? "I said. "Mama, *please*. You are frightening me.

"Then don't drag behind me. Hold my hand and keep up. Nothing's going to bother you if you don't look back," Mama said.

Mama told us the same stories every Friday night, not because the ghost was real, but because she had to get back home before she was missed.

Daddy played two or three hundred dollars in numbers weekly (bolito), yet, we had a hard time getting him to buy an ice cream or candy bar for us.

Mama made our candy—peanut brittle or sugar-covered pecans and the best ice cream in the whole world. I think one of the reasons Grandpa was so crazy about Mama was for her good cooking. Grandpa often walked down the hill to our house to get something sweet to eat from Mama. He loved biscuits and sweets.

Thank you God. If I had to choose between all the mothers in the world, I would choose my mama.

Grandma's and Grandpa's house was a house that spoke for itself. Daddy was born in that house and continues to live there. The living room was decorated with a burgundy velvet settee, two matching velvet chairs, a piano, a beautiful mahogany bed and a fireplace. No one in the family could play the piano, and no one was allowed too touch the piano.

A hallway separated the front room from the rooms shared by Auntie M., Ellawease and Grandma. Grandpa slept in the next room.

I thought, as a child, they slept in different bedrooms because Grandpa called out in his sleep for his girlfriend all night and every night. Without shame, Grandpa would repeat it over and over. "O-h-o-o, Sarah. O-h-o-o Sarah. I do wish I had married Sarah. "

Grandma seemed untouched by his reminiscing. She never said a word. I thought maybe they were too old to sleep together. I realized that Grandpa had his own way of punishing Grandma by calling out another woman's name all night.

Grandma's house was the only house with a radio. She allowed us to listen to the radio twice a day if we were there. At night it was stories of the Canadian Mounties, and at 5:00 PM week days, the local radio station played one hour of black music. The "Jive to Five," it was called.

Toney, Ellawease and I would dance the whole hour, even though we had no ideal what kind of dancing we should be doing. When no one was around I would look in the back of the battery radio, trying to see if I could find the people who were doing the talking. I couldn't figure it out. I didn't dare ask anyone why I couldn't see the people. I was to afraid they would laugh at me.

Chapter Nineteen

MR. BULLDOG, AS WE called him, had wooden legs. He was the uncle of Lillie Mae (Fat, the bouncer). He lived around the corner with his mother. Everyday he walked around to our house. It was a five minute walk that took him thirty minutes.

Mr. Bulldog, never came inside because he hadn't mastered the art of walking up the steps on his wooden legs. He used his walking stick to bang on the porch to let Mama know he was there.

Bam-bam-bam, we would hear. Then, in a loud voice, "Miz Lucille, Miz. Lucille." Mama new what he wanted. "Just a minute Bulldog," Mama said.

Mama would serve him with a half pint of moonshine on the porch.

"Miz Lucille, would you fix me something too eat? he always asked.

"Fish or chicken?" Mama said.

"Fish with potato salad," he said.

Bulldog ate and drank on the porch every day.

Mrs. Irene, Bulldog's mother, came everyday for her "medicine" (moonshine). Mrs. Irene was seventy-nine years old and walked faster and straighter than any young person I knew. Mama would write letters for her, read her mail to her and help her count her money, because neither she nor Bulldog could read or write.

Mrs. Irene wouldn't come for a drink if Mr. Bulldog was there. She didn't want him to know she drank. Of course, he knew anyway. When Bulldog didn't feel like walking to our house for his food and drink, he would send Mrs. Irene, and Mama would drive her back home. Irene knew that Mama delivered dinners every day at noontime and she would be able to get a ride home. Everything seemed to work so easily. No one was just takers. Everyone seemed to be givers *and* takers.

Then there was Harry. He looked almost white, with scary looking green eyes and nappy hair. In my mind I thought that Harry was the very image of the kind of person that had escaped from prison or maybe from a mental hospital Harry came by everyday to chop wood and keep the yard clean. In return, Mama provided his food. She would make Harry pay for his drinks. I was afraid of Harry. He looked so different. Harry had to be a killer, I thought. I had never seen a black person look like that.

Mama didn't allow me to have friends over if she wasn't at home. That was fine with me, because I didn't want my friends to know how we lived. Harry wouldn't say one word to me if Mama, wasn't at home, and if my friends stopped by, Harry would surly tell Mama. I often thought that Harry was a spy for Mama, planted there to keep an eye on me when she wasn't at home, pretending he was working in the yard.

"G'anna, you know what Miz Lucille said. I'm going to tell her about the kids coming over today," Harry said.

"I didn't know they were coming," I said. You can tell her anything you want to." I felt I couldn't breathe without someone watching me. Mr. Johnson sat on his front porch across the street, pretending he was sleeping in that chair with his cap pulled over his eyes. I know he's watching everything that goes on over here. If he only knew I was watching him too.

Vera told me about him. The lady around the corner had twin girls by him. "He should be ashamed," I thought. Mr. Johnson was a longshoreman. He was sixty-five years old, with skin blacker than night, with teeth as pretty as pearls—very neat and very handsome. He was a mean man, according to Mama. I think Mama felt that he was mean because he mistreated his wife. I respected Mama's thoughts and feelings about people and was very carefully to remembering them.

"G'anna, come here, come here, quick. " Vera said one day. "See Mr. Johnson, on the corner talking to that young lady? He's talking about something fresh," she said.

"How do you know that, Vera?"

"Watch the movements of the woman," she said. "See how she's kicking in the dirt as she talks. I bet you a dollar," Vera said.

She walked up to Mr. Johnson and asked, "What were you talking to that lady about? She was kicking a hole in that dirt." Mr. Johnson only walked away laughing and went into his house. A month later he died while having sex in his house with the same lady.

There was also Shuman. Shuman, I didn't like very much. He was the mechanic who kept our car running. He worked at the gas station up the street, a very sly, quiet person who couldn't look you in the eyes. All these things changed for Shuman with one drink. Then, he wouldn't stop talking, and bothering everyone. He was the only one that got on Mama's nerves. She would have to put him out once his personality changed, because she couldn't control him. He was really quite harmless. He just talked too much.

Mama's customers were very respectful of her. They all had a line of credit and had to pay on Friday or Saturday for the food and drinks for the week. If they didn't show up, Mama and Toney would get in the car and find them.

Chapter Twenty

I GOT MARRIED WHEN I was nineteen. Yes, I married Bud Sommerset, the boy next door, only he wasn't next door anymore. He was getting out of the army.

Mama insisted that Bud ask Daddy's permission. I couldn't understand why Mama felt the need to have him go all the way in the country to ask a man that had never done anything other than treat us worse than he treated strangers for my hand in marriage.

I could have died. "Mama," I asked, "why do we need too ask Daddy if I can get married? Daddy doesn't care anything about us. He's not helping you pay the bills for the wedding. Why do we have too do this, Mama? I don't even want him their. Let Toney, walk me down the isle. What if Daddy comes in drunk and acting wild and talking loud? Please Mama, I don't want him at my wedding," I said.

"We don't have to do wrong because he doesn't know how to do right," Mama replied. "He's your father, and that's not going to change. He will be invited to walk you down the isle. Whether he will do it or not is a different thing. Now stop whimpering about it. "

The Sunday for our trip to the country came. The boy next door, Mama and I drove the hundred miles in the country to get Daddy's permission.

Daddy started walking through the woods.

"Come on y'all," he said.

We had to almost run to keep up with him. Finally we were able to walk along beside him and Bud asked for my hand in marriage.

Daddy said yes.

I thought to myself, "It doesn't matter a damn with me what you say. You can't tell me what too do. I'm only here because of Mama. You are not helping to pay for the wedding and furthermore you haven't paid or given me a dime in years. Damn what you say. It's only out of respect for Mama that we are asking you at all. "

Thirty-seven years have passed, and I am still bitter with Daddy. He never took responsibility for anything other than himself. Somehow it just doesn't seem fair. Two of the people he threw away a long time ago have to take care of him now: Toney and I. Toney drives a hundred miles or more a week—sometimes twice a week—to take care of Daddy's shopping, making sure he's clean and to take care of him the best that we can. After we take him shopping for food, he will not allow us to help put the food in the refrigerator. Because he has lived a life of tricks he doesn't trust anyone.

"Sit it on the porch, and I'll put it up," he says.

"You may forget to put it in the refrigerator, and I'll find it sitting here just like the last time we came," Toney answers.

"Leave the damn shit on the porch. I can put my own groceries up," Daddy said. I don't need no damn body to help me. I have been looking out for myself all my life." He was convinced he didn't need anyone, but someone had to help him find his way home on occasion. His sister and her children would have taken his land away from him if not for Toney and me. I had Daddy's ninety five year old sister arrested in May of 1997. She and her son cut $60,000 worth of timber from the family estate. I am the bad guy now, of course. I don't mind being the bad guy, if I have to. Mama always said that If you believe in something, you should stand up for it. And I believe it was wrong for Auntie to think she was the sole beneficiary of more than two thousand acres of land.

Mama is the place "from whence cometh my strength." Mama was passive but not weak—passive because she thought there was good in the worst of us and bad in the best of us. Mama was kind to Auntie's children. The college professor's wife's sisters, when they were in college and got into serious trouble, came to Mama for help and received it.

I read somewhere that children choose their parents before conception. My mother would have been my choice, but I would not have chosen a father who did not love his family. There are times when I would not like to be related too anyone, especially to Daddy. Still, there is a reason for everything,. I am who I am today because of what I was yesterday.

Thank you God .

Chapter Twenty-One

HIGH SCHOOL WAS REFRESHING. I was very comfortable in knowing we were never going back to Daddy. I was invited to the prom as a junior, and had a great time. The night the senior prom was scheduled the weather was so bad, the school announced on the radio that the prom was canceled.

My date, another couple, and I were riding in the car on our way to the prom when we heard the announcement.

"I know we are not going back home," Willis said

"I sneaked my change of clothes out yesterday," said Zelda.

"If I go back home to change, I'm not going too be able to leave," I said.

"I was afraid of that," said Zelda. "I sneaked some of my clothes out for you. It's prom night. We planned to party before there was a storm," she said.

Wallace was chewing gum and laughing softly. "Tell your mother it's prom night," said Wallace. "It's p-a-r-t-y time. "

I was afraid of the consequences, but I wanted to have a fun time as well as my friends, and we did. We went to an adult nightclub with borrowed I. D. cards and danced until 2 AM.

"It's two o'clock in the morning," I exclaimed. "Mama is going to kill me. I got to get home. Wallace, get Willis and Zelda, and let's get out of here. "

I changed back to my prom dress in the car as we wondered what we were going to tell Mama. I was counting on the fact that Mama trusted my friends. They were very respectable kids who enjoyed having good clean fun such as it was in the sixties.

Mama was waiting. She turned the porch light on before Willis could turn the lights off on the car.

"What are you going to tell her? Zelda said.

"The truth," I said.

We went in. Mama didn't allow me to sit around in a car. She said it didn't look good. Wallace spoke up. "Mrs. Sharpe, it's my fault that G'anna is late getting home. I know you heard on the radio that the prom was cancelled," Wallace said.

I could see on Mama's face that Wallace had defused her by telling her that half-truth. "My grandmother gave me a surprise graduation party," Wallace continued.

Why didn't Wallace stop while he was ahead, I worried. That didn't sound right. I hoped he didn't think Mama was going to buy that. But she did.

"Pick you up on Sunday at ten for church," Wallace said to me.

Later, I lay in bed thinking what a wonderful time I had had and how wonderfully different life was now. I couldn't help but think about the lie Wallace told Mama. I couldn't believe Mama had fallen for it.

"It was my prom," I thought, "and that's why Mama didn't

get on me about the time." I knew not to try that again.

"Thank you God," I prayed. Thank you for my life-long friends. Thank you for the Smith family Mama works for. I would have been unable to attend the prom as a junior or senior if Mrs. Smith had not loaned me her daughter's prom gown. Thank you for allowing me to graduate. I only wish Daddy cared enough to attend the ceremony."

Chapter Twenty-Two

DADDY'S LIFE CONTINUED TO be filled with alcohol, women and fast cars long after we were adults He never wanted to know his grandkids and his grands didn't want to get to know him. They were afraid of him.

It was summer of 1977 when the phone ring. It was Toney. "Sis, Auntie just called. Daddy's in the hospital in the country and needs to be transferred to the hospital near us. They are unable to treat him in that hospital because they don't have the proper equipment," he said.

"Why is she calling us?" I asked. What's wrong with him?"

"He had another car wreck," Toney said.

"And he didn't get killed? I replied.

"Don't be so mean, Sis," he said. "He didn't get killed but some woman in the car with him did. "

"I bet she was as drunk as he probably was," I said.

"You are probably right, Sis, but what are we going too do about it?" Toney asked.

"What are we going too do about it?" I replied. "Nothing! What would he have done if it was one of us. ? Nothing !"

"Well, Mama said we should go and see abou Toney replied. .

"Mama said! Mama said! Has Mama lost her mir

I could hear Toney laughing softly over the phone, but it was not funny to me. "I don't want any part of the whole got damn thing," I said. "They all call when there is a problem with him and they think they may end up having to take care of him, but when they are all stealing and selling timber off the estate no one says anything at all to us. They think Mama may sue him for money she never received in the first place," I said. "No I am not going," I declared, and hung up the phone.

Five minutes later Mama called.

"Hook, I understand how you feel, but he is your Daddy," she said.

"I know that, I answered, "but I think you forgot to tell him.

"The woman that got killed in the car with him has a husband." Mama said.

"And you want us too go see about him? Mama, this is not out of disrespect for you, but have you lost your mind," I asked. "Let her husband go and finish killing him."

We arrived about nine that morning to find that he was still lying on the gurney in the emergency room of the country hospital. We had him transferred to one of the low country hospitals, where they found he had several broken ribs, one of them threatening another organ.

The shock came when he had to go home with one of us. That's where Mama drew the line. She wasn't going to let him stay with her. Toney's marriage was on the rocks, so Daddy couldn't stay with him. It only left me.

I was distraught. Would I never be free of this man? I called Bud at work and explained what was going on. Before I could finish explaining, Bud said. "He can't stay with us. He's to damn sorry. He doesn't want anything from life, and if you fool with him we won't have anything in life. No. Let him go with the people he's having a good time with. "

"Bud, I think it's to late to say no," I replied. He's down here in the emergency room and can't go home alone until he heals. I don't want him any more than you do, but he can't stay with Mama and Toney. What else can we do?"

Chapter Twenty-Three

BUD WAS RAISED BY an aunt, one of many relatives she raised. The last one—Jan—she raised from three years old until she was sixteen.

One Sunday while Bud was doing his three weeks of army reserve training, my girls and I stopped by his aunt's house, as we often did after church.

"Mom, can Jan spend the night with us?" my daughter Mich asked me

I tried to pretend that I didn't hear her.

"Mom, p-l-e-a-s-e, can Jan spend the night with us," Angel chimed in.

Everyone was looking right at my mouth. I had no choice but too say yes. The weekend passed and a new week began. I begin wondering, but only the girls and I were at home until Bud got back. I thought they would call for me to bring her home soon. They always did.

One week went by, with no call from Bud's family, and Jan never mentioned going home.

"Jan, I think you need to call home," I said.

"I did," she said.

"She didn't tell you to come home?" I asked.

"No! She said it was alright," she said.

I thought to myself that something was not right. They

usually worried me to death to bring her home when she's over here.

Two weeks went by. At the end of the third week Bud finally came home from his reserve duty. I explained to him everything that was going on. No one had called bout Jan.

Bud wasted no time calling. Then he turned to me. "Can you believe it? They put her out," Bud said.

Bud and I sat down and had a serious discussion about what we were going to do. We certainly did not need another person too take care of.

"Well, God sometimes tests you in many ways," Bud said. I didn't have a mother or father. I was just one of the kids my aunt raised. I think the Lord is trying to tell me I need to give something back," he said.

"I don't agree with you, but I do understand," I said to him. "We both had a hard life. We will try to do the best we can. It's going too be very hard with the girls in private school and going into junior high" I said, "and they won't even tell you why they put her out. "

Chapter Twenty-Four

WE BROUGHT DADDY HOME from the hospital. We didn't have enough room, nor could we afford him. We did the best we could. Bud was already working day and night. The kids didn't want him there. Jan was there and we didn't understand why or quite how she got there. I was doing the best I could, pretending I could handle it all, but it was really too much. I was working for the Department of Human Resources, and I talked with my supervisor about the whole situation. She suggested I file for foster care services for Jan. It would repay me for any clothing we purchased and give me two dollars a day for meals.

Jan was in the 11th grade. The neighbors begin reporting to me that Jan was going from one to the other trying to borrow money.

I confronted her with this. "Jan the neighbors are telling me that you are trying to borrow money from them when I am at work," I said.

She said she had done no such thing.

"I don't know if it's true or not," I continued, "but we don't borrow anything from our neighbors. We are all on very good terms, and I would like for it to continue that way if you don't mind. "

The kids were complaining about her mistreating them

while we were working. I gave Jan ten dollars a week lowance and asked her not to tell the girls that she rece. a larger amount for her allowance than they did. Well! Th. was another problem. Of course she couldn't keep her mouth closed.

It was almost the end of the school year. Her teacher was reporting to me that Jan was skipping school. The problems were getting too big for us to handle. I was trying to raise two girls of my own, and they didn't need to see this kind of be- havior in the house where we lived.

What was I going to do? Meanwhile, another event brought things to a head. I had a cash box in my closet with silver coins and silver dollars in it. I even had a two dollar bill, a five dol- lar silver certificate and some regular dollar bills in it. In all, it contained about $300. The box was locked, and I had the key on my key ring.

I picked the box up to add another five dollar silver certifi- cate to it, and discovered that the box was empty. I screamed. The money belonged to my mother. She had been saving coins since the sixties, when I was in college, and the box was kept locked and on the closet shelf.

"Jan," I said. "Where is my money?" I threw the empty box on the bed.

"Where is my money?" I asked again.

She didn't ask what money. "I don't have your money," she said.

I was so angry. I began packing her clothes as fast as I could. Angel and Mich asked what was wrong.

'ther's money and coins are missing," I

\me I had all of Jan clothes sitting in
\jr.

\jng on?" he asked. I explained to him and said,
\jne goes or I will. "

Bud put Jan and her clothes in the car and drove her to her mother's—a mother that had two other daughters, neither of whom she raised. One was raised in foster care, the other was raised by her father and his wife. Jan's mother was not a responsible person. She lived from here too there, was always in fights and was an alcoholic. This was going to be Jan's new life, because her aunt would not take her back.

Bud's aunt taught school in a small town nearby, but to far too travel home everyday. Jan lived and attended school there also. They shared a house with a cousin and her son whose living and traveling circumstances were the same.

Bud's cousin didn't attend church on Sunday, which meant Bud had to take her communion to her. One Sunday his cousin asked, "Bud, why did your aunt give Jan too G'anna and you? That girl is too much for you guys to handle."

"We could never get them to tell us what happened," Bud said.

"Well, I'll tell you why," his cousin said. "The neighbors were reporting that Jan was leaving school and sneaking boys and alcohol in when Auntie went to her class. People were telling Auntie for the longest time, and she didn't believe them. As a matter of fact Auntie got in a real bad argument because she didn't believe her friend. Two days later Auntie forgot her roll book and had to return home to pick it up. Well, what she found was more than a roll book. She caught Jan in bed with two guys and alcohol," Cousin said. There was money missing from Auntie's pocketbook. By the time Auntie found all of this out, she was feeling embarrassed, and that's how you got her. That's what it was all about," Cousin said. "They should have told you something. You guys are to young to handle her. "

I reported this to the foster care worker, and she gave me a chance to read Jan's file. In the file I read that Jan was accusing my Daddy of making sexual advances toward her during the recovery time he lived with us. I thought I was going to faint. Daddy had recovered from the accident, gone home, and never thanked us for helping him or letting him live with us for six weeks. We never heard from him again until two years later, when he needed to have gall bladder surgery.

Life has taught me so many things, mostly about people: they are not real, they are not true and honorable to anyone anymore. There are some who are, but very few.

Fran, my dear friend of twenty-five years was one of them. I tried to hide most things from her, because she had her own share of problems. Her mother had died in child birth. Her sweet grandmother raised her and her sister.

Her father had married the woman next door, the story goes, started a new family before the mother was cold in the grave, and moved to New Jersey.

After high school Fran went off on one of those live-in

jobs, all the way to Vermont.

"Fran, how can you go so far to work for the first time. Aren't you afraid?" I asked.

"Of course I'm afraid," she answered. "But what else can I do here? I got to help my grandmother get my brother Serlin through high school," she said.

"What about your daddy? Can't he help?" I asked.

"I don't want to live with them. They have their own daughter, and he doesn't want us." Fran said.

"How does your grandmother feel about this," I asked.

"She's alright with it. When I save my money I am going to send for Granny. She's getting too old to live alone, and besides there's nothing to keep us from leaving this town. "

My heart was broken. Fran was the one person I shared all my silliness with and all my thoughts about boys and sex, hopes and dreams. What was I supposed to do? Who was I supposed to talk with.

"You know you can come visit with me when I get settled," Fran said as though she knew what I was thinking.

"When are you leaving ?" I asked.

"Next week," Fran said. "I am not lying, G'anna. I will write you. "

I thought too myself, "She's not going to write me. She will forget about me once she's in New York or Vermont or wherever she is.

Chapter Twenty-Five

FRAN WAS ALWAYS A girl of her word. She called once a month. One year after taking her new job she began having really weird dreams that we often talked about.

I wanted to know if she were sure that it was a dream. She said she was, adding, "G'anna, I am not crazy!"

"I would move from there if I were you," I said. "It all sounds so scary. "

"There's no reason to get frightened. I just feel that there is something there, watching me, when I wake up. "

"Please tell the people you work for, Fran. That's scary. What does it look like?"

"It's a man, and he's always standing over me watching me when I wake up. At first I was afraid, but not any more, because it has happened too many times, and I know he's not real.

"That's the part that's frightening," I replied. "Maybe he's your angel, since you are so far from home. Maybe he's watching you because you are sick or something. Are you alright?" I asked.

"I am fine G'anna. I met a guy from Georgia, and I am going into the city for two weeks on my vacation. Stop worrying. I'm alright."

"I'll try," I said, "but it's all too strange for me. I wouldn't stay there another minute. "

Six months later we both had a secret to tell each other. We were pregnant.

"Fran, what are you going to do?" I said. "Are you getting married?"

"No! I don't want to get married." She said. "I will one day. First, I have to get Granny settled. Granny's going to keep the baby once it's born. I am moving into the city. I got a job with New York Bell. I'll be able to move Granny up here with me soon, and maybe then if we are still together we will get married. "

"Who is this person?" I asked. "Are you sure he's not married all ready?"

"No, he's not married. He's divorced with children. He's ten years older than I am, has his own business and waits on me hand and foot. We are going to live together for now. Is that enough information for you, lady?" Fran said.

"I suppose, for now anyway, but I am sure I will have plenty more questions."

"What about you?" Fran asked. .

"Well! You knew Bud and I had planned to get married anyway when he returned home. So April is the date," I replied. "Are you coming?"

"I am not ready for questions, G'anna. Will you forgive me if I don't?"

"Of course. You are my friend and I love you."

Our child-bearing brought Fran and me closer, and our children brought us closer still. Two years later she managed to move her grandmother and her sister to Yonkers, New York.

Fran was a health nut. She got on me all the time about not eating right.

"What difference does it make if we don't eat right," I laughed. "According to statistics women with small breasts will die anyway from breast cancer."

"I guess you and I are as good as dead," she said. "And I got a little more than you."

We thought it was so funny. As we laughed I replied, "Has anyone ever asked you for more breast?"

It was August. Fran was on the floor exercising and gave herself a breast examination. She found a lump. In December, 1980, Fran died. She was thirty-nine years old.

Thank you, God, for the time we had together.

Chapter Twenty-Six

I HATE IT WHEN the phone rings and Daddy's relatives are telling me what we need to do for him: he needs a car, or he's too far in the woods not to have a car, or he has no one to talk to. My first thought always is, "Who called us when we needed something as simple as food?"

Daddy's sister called. "Y'all need to take that car from your daddy. He's driving too slow on the road. If another car or truck comes over a hill and he's driving that slow it's going to be one bad accident," she said.

I thought to myself, "I wish she would make up her mind. We just bought the car. Now she's saying take the car. She doesn't call when her sons are renting his land out for hunting and never gives the money toward his care. Get off my back, old woman. You weren't concerned about what happened too Mama or Toney and me. Now you want us to remove him from there so you and your family can have the run of the place. It will never happen as long as I am alive"

Grandpa predicted that she and her family would try to steal the whole estate. There were many times I overheard Grandpa talking about how Auntie A.'s husband fought him about his own land on Grandpa's own front porch. Auntie A.'s husband never had a pot too piss in until he married Auntie A.

Grandpa gave them 135 acres of land. He moved her and her family into another county in 1924 in a mule-drawn wagon, hoping that it would eliminate some of the problems they were causing him. The same problems continue today.

Jackie, Auntie A.'s son, called one day about the pine straw on Daddy's place. He wanted to rake it up and sell it. Jackie has been raking it for years, free, but now Toney and I need the money to help take care of Daddy. Jackie tells us he wants to pay us after selling the straw. Jackie doesn't know that I know that he wouldn't pay Jesus himself.

"Jackie, you will have to pay up front," I said.

"Why do I have too pay up front. Uncle Son never made me pay up front," he said.

"That's right; and you wouldn't pay him," I said.

"Why do you have to come and change things," he said.

"Pay up front or leave it alone, and if you rake it without my permission I will have you arrested," I replied.

When I had the warrant taken out on Jackie and his mother for selling timber that belonged to the estate, one of the judges told me that Jackie owed everybody in the county. One man threatened to kill him because he wouldn't pay for some seed and grain he had gotten.

"Jackie," I said, "it doesn't matter how Daddy and you handled things before Toney and I came into the picture. Now it will be handled my way or no way. Your mother has been calling and calling for us to look after Daddy's affairs. We cannot afford to take care of him out of our pocket and let you continue to make your living off his land. Before going to court, I tried talking to you. I even tried talking with your mother and she hung the phone up on me. At that time I only wanted you to pay him enough to buy his snuff or tobacco and gas for his car. If you won't do that, what makes you think that I believe you will pay after you have sold the straw? I am sorry, but you will have to pay one thousand dollars before you rake one pile of straw," I said.

Jackie didn't know it, but I had seen the eighteen-wheel truck full of Daddy's straw three days before when I was there to carry Daddy to the doctor. I had been out pricing the straw and knew what the price should be.

"As a matter of fact, Jackie," I said, "I would rather not deal with you at all."

"I'm not paying you all a damn thing," Jackie said. I will pay it to Uncle Son the same as always."

"Daddy's mind is getting bad. This way it will eliminate doubt," I said to Jackie.

I could see that Jackie was determined to do things his way. Jackie's sister called, and so did his brother, his mother and Jackie himself. But my mind was made up. I decided I didn't need this problem in my life.

"G'anna, what seems to be the problem?" asked the professor's wife.

"Who said there was a problem?" I replied.

"I talked with my mother," she said.

"What did she say," I replied. "Did she tell you that she hung the phone up in my face? I really don't have anything else to say," I continued. "When I wanted to talk, no one wanted to talk to me. I have set the rules that Toney and I will operate by, and that's that. I have done all the talking I'm going to do. If Jackie bothers anything on Daddy's land without paying, I will have the thief jailed. The family has gathered together many times trying to settle the estate. Auntie A.'s family fights it every time. Why agree to settle the estate when your family can make a good living on the land of dead family member and of the family members who live in other places and know very little about the history of the land."

Auntie A.'s children have lots of quit claim deeds that are not legal that they bought from other family members that only wanted a fast buck. Once the estate is settled, the quit claim deeds will be no good. Some one may even end up in jail.

Grandpa was twelve years old when they freed the slaves. Before his mother died the person that had owned them promised to look after her two boys and kept the promise. Grandpa began buying farmland in 1897. By 1955 he had acquired more than 2,000 acres of land.

Each time he made a purchase he made it in a white man's name and later the man would change the deed to Grandpa's name. It has become one of the largest land holdings in the county. Between family and the whites in the area trying to take the land, there were many times when I wished that I wasn't involved in such a mess. But when I really think about it, I realize I am who I am and what I am because of where I came from.

Now that I have put a stop to most of the stealing Aun-

tie A. and her boys were doing—from Daddy and from the estate—they won't even go by his house to see how he is doing.

Daddy was also a very dishonest man who never told the
truth about anything. He didn't know Mama very well. She
was a proud lady.

"Mama, I heard that Daddy made a lot of money selling
timber last week," I would say. "Why don't you have the law
make him help us."

"Sit down and let me explain something too you," she
said. "We don't want nothing that he doesn't want us to have.
Do you understand?"

"Yes, Mama, but it's still wrong," I replied.

"Always remember. He will need you and Toney before
you need him," she said. "Stop worrying. You will make yourself sick. "

"Life is very complicated, Mama. "

"It doesn't have to be complicated, Honey," Mama said.
"You have to learn the difference between the important and
unimportant, the things you have control over and the things
you don't, the things you can change and the things you can't.
Try not to worry about the decisions you choose to make.
Make them fairly, and you will do fine."

Chapter Twenty-Seven

I AM THINKING HOW wonderful it was to see things through a child's eyes, to mix sugar with water and drink it for lemonade, put sugar on bread and eat it for peanut butter, make the chickens move off the eggs and cook the eggs for hamburgers, wander through the fields when you are at your lowest point and find a beautiful peach tree loaded with the largest, sweetest, peaches you have ever seen or tasted.

I have tried many times to find that tree again, and if I had not shared the peaches with Mama I would have believed it was only a dream.

How great God is. He provides us with what we need as children and as adults. If I had a chance to live parts of my life over, I would. But not my childhood. It was lonely, hard, and scary. "Thank you, God, for Mama," I thought. "If Toney and I had not had her, Toney would be dead."

Toney was growing very slowly and wasn't a well child. When he was nine, the doctor told Mama that he had a bad heart and needed to have open heart surgery. "Mrs. Sharpe, I have made arrangements for your son's surgery at the Medical College Of Georgia for next Wednesday," he told Mama. "The hospital wants him there the day before the surgery. Ask at the admitting office, and they will take it from there".

Mama was scared. She prayed all night long for the Lord

to tell her what to do. It didn't make any difference one way or the other with Daddy. He would have one less mouth to feed.

The hospital was more than two hours away from where we lived. Daddy was nowhere to be found when the time came to drive Mama and Toney to Augusta for the operation. Mama and Toney, carrying a brown paper bag full of their clothes, walked to the highway to catch a ride with Mr. Almond, the mailman who doubled as a taxi cab.

I was afraid to stay behind with Grandma. What if I wet her bed? For some reason that was my greatest fear when I had to stay with her. Before going to bed Grandma would always say, "Gal, make sure you use the pot before going to sleep. If you wet the bed your ass will be mine." The truth was, I had never wet the bed.

Mama and Toney rode the Trailway Bus to Augusta. Georgia. They arrived later in the afternoon than scheduled, but in time. The next afternoon, though, Mama and Toney came walking up the road to the house.

"Lucille! I thought Toney's operation was scheduled for eight o'clock this morning," Grandma said.

"It was," Mama said. "I prayed for God to give me an answer, and I decided not to let the Medical College of Georgia hospital experiment on my child. I made him get out of that bed and get dressed. We came home. He will live as he is."

"I hope you know what you are doing," Grandma said.

"I know my child was crying, and I know I was scared. We will take what comes," Mama said.

Toney is still a short man, but he is sixty years old and healthy. Thank you, God, for my big brother .

I am not sure from whence Mama's strength came. I realized through the years that Mama was an unsinkable person. Mama's mother fell dead with a stroke on a Sunday, and I was born on the following Monday. I never got to know the strength of Big Mama.

My strength rushes over me some days, and some days it recedes to the bad times all over again. As an adult I am sometimes depressed to realize that sugar and water are not lemonade, bread and sugar not peanut butter, and eggs are not hamburgers

Yesterday is an illusion that one can never see again. Tomorrow may bring similar events and difficulties, but the day will never be the same. People seem the same sometimes, faces look the same, odors sometimes smell the same but it's all only a reminder of where we've been.

Chapter Twenty-Eight

IT WAS 1962, THE year of my wedding. Two days after Bud and I got married he went to Washington D. C., looking for work and found a job selling vacuum cleaners. Not being good at the sale of vacuum cleaners he returned to Georgia a month later. He went back to the job that he held before he went into the army as an engraver at one of the local jewelry stores and enrolled in college again.

One month later we moved to the east side of town in a low-rent district. There we lived for two-and-a-half miserable years in an upstairs, one-bedroom, hot apartment. The best thing about living in that apartment was watching the ships go down the Savannah river from our bathroom window.

I was unemployed, pregnant, lonely, and nineteen years old. I spent my days at Mama's and nights watching Bud study. Meanwhile, my stomach grew like a pumpkin.

Bud needed only two years to complete his four year degree. He attended school mornings and worked evenings. His weekly pay was $27. 00 a week for a wife and the two children we now had. The youngest child was allergic to milk. The soybean milk she drank was forty-nine cents a can—very expensive in 1963. We were barely making it.

The new baby had come in December. Bud graduated in June, and our rent was being raised from forty-seven dollars a month too ninety dollars a month. Something had to be done fast.

"G'anna, the housing authority will allow us to live here until January. I can't see paying the Housing Authority that kind of money for something we will never own," Bud said. "I will began teaching in September. We need to start looking for a house that we can afford."

They were building a new area on the west side of town for blacks and we purchased our first home for fourteen thousand dollars. Bud received his first teaching check and came home with his head hanging down.

"What's wrong? What's wrong with you, Bud?" I asked.

"I spent all that time in school, all those hours studying, trying to better myself, and I am only bringing home two hundred and seventy-five dollars a month," Bud said. "How will we live on this with a house payment of one hundred and one dollars?"

"Bud, we have made it on a lot less. Things will work out," I reassured him.

"How will they work out?" he asked sceptically.

"I'll get job," I replied.

"I want you to stay home and raise the girls. I'll find part-time work," Bud said.

Bud worked full time and part time until both girls finished college. He retired from the army reserve and never complained, not one time. Thank you, God, for Bud.

The girls were not without music lessons, dance lessons —all the things they needed to help them in life. At the age of fourteen the my oldest daughter was the pianist for three churches, and at the age of seventeen she had plans to attend Indiana University. We had no idea that her college would consume our life savings.

"G'anna, I won't be able to take off from my second job to drive Angel to Indiana. Do you think the two of you can manage?" Bud said. "I will map the route out for you," he said.

Angel was excited. She couldn't wait to go to college.

"Daddy I can drive all the way to Indiana and Mom will only have to drive back. When she gets tried, she can spend the night in a motel," Angel said.

"Angel, it takes money to spend the night in a motel. We can barely afford to take you there at all," I replied.

"G'anna, do you think you can get one of your friends to help you drive?" Bud asked. "We can buy all the food and pay for the room. "

So I asked my friend Patricia to go on the trip with us. Angel talked all the way—more than fourteen hours. I was worrying about possibly not having enough money. We had no idea that there would be wall-to-wall kids and parents there to bring their kids to college and did not make reservations at any motel. All the motels within in a fifty mile range were full.

"Don't get excited, G'anna," Patricia said. "If worse comes too worst we can sleep in the car."

I wanted to tell her we couldn't afford to drive another fifty miles and have enough money to get back home, but instead I prayed. The owner of the last boarding house we stopped at called ahead to one of her friends that had a small room with one small bed and a wash room. I apologized to Patricia all night for the inconveniences

"Look G'anna, stop worrying about it. One day when I am married and have kids you can return the favor," Patricia said.

Angel and Patricia slept in the bed, one at the head of the bed and one at the foot. I slept on the floor. The next morning, we got Angel settled on campus and began our long and lonely trip back home without my daughter. I have never stopped worrying about her well-being.

Angel went through those four years like a champ and sailed right into medical school. She made us very proud.

The next year Bud carried Mick to the University of Georgia at Athens on a Wednesday. We knew that Mick would never go far away to college because she never wanted to be more than four or five hours away from home. Mick loves home and family.

On Thursday afternoon Mick called home. "Mom, I don't like it here. Please come get me," she pleaded.

"I can't come for you. You must go to college if you want to make money in this world," I told her. But she wasn't buying it.

"I am sick, Mom. I can't make it here."

"Sick? What's wrong?" I asked.

"It's my breasts. They are hard like a rock," Mick explained.

I knew Mick had fibrositis, but I had never heard of breasts turning hard on anyone.

"Mick, I am going to call the doctor," I told her. The doctor called in medication for her, and soon she got better. But Mick was never happy away at school. It was one thing after the other—too many people on the public bus, the kids weren't friendly, the work was too hard, she needed a room without a roommate, she couldn't study, she didn't like the food. It began affecting me.

"G'anna get Mick on the phone," Bud said. "She will stay in that school. I work day and night to give them the best education we can afford, and she will stay in college." He said it and he meant it.

Mick graduated from college four and a half years later with honors. She cooped with the justice department during her four years of college and was employed by them after college. She went on to become one of the best business persons in the world.

Thank you, God.

Chapter Twenty-Nine

I ALWAYS TRIED TO make Mama's birthday very special, even as a child. After getting home from school one birthday, I rushed inside, put my books down, and ran five blocks to the shopping center with my baby-sitting money I had saved to buy a birthday gift for her. It was the first gift I remember buying Mama, and I was so proud of it. It was a small ceramic cow with detachable parts. The milk jugs could either hang off to the side or be left off. I gave her birthday cards, too. Each card give her directions to finding her gift. Mama had so much fun trying to find it. She would laugh and laugh each time she would find a note. Finally she found the gift.

"O-o-o, my little girl, you didn't have to spend your money on me," Mama said.

"Mama, you are worth that and more. I just don't have any more," I replied. I was always trying to make Mama happy in every way I knew how, because she had been through so much.

One day I realized I had grown into a person I didn't recognize any more, trying to meet the needs of everyone else. I was living for my mother, my kids, my husband and anyone with a problem or anyone needing help for any reason. My life had turned into a life of service, but somewhere along the way I forgot myself and my own needs, hopes, and dreams.

I feel at times disconnected, as though the world and everything in it is my enemy. I feel lost, hopeless and helpless, stumbling along trying to find my way in the dark with people watching me. I know they are there, but I can't see them. They are waiting for me to stumble and fall. They are quiet; they can feel and see the fear in me as I reach out with my hands trying to feel my way just a little at a time. At such times I am afraid to reach out too far because I am scared that I am not smart enough, not pretty enough, not good enough. I am not supposed to let the world know or see my pain, my fears, my sorrows.

Then there are other days when I can't be defeated by anyone or anything, when there is nothing I can't do, when there are no fears, just strength. Now I find myself wondering at age fifty-eight, "Where do I go from here? The kids are all grown, and Bud's retired. I don't have to worry about the unfairness in the school system, about people who couldn't handle the presence of a strong black man."

Unlike so many others, Bud can still look in the mirror every morning and be proud of what he sees, and now that Mama is dead I have to take a look at myself. I don't have to worry or feel the need to be a care giver, and I am sometimes revisited by all the fears that were a part of my life as a child. I never want to be hungry again, never live in a house in which I can lie in bed and see the stars through the roof, never be afraid again of having to run and hide and of fear itself, yet all those old fears seem to overtake me at times as through it were yesterday.

Toney visits with Daddy once, sometimes twice, a week. "G'anna, I don't know how much longer Daddy will be able to live alone," he told me. "I asked him to come live with me."

"I can tell you what his answer was," I said. "He's never going to leave his house."

Toney agreed with me, but continued to explain his concerns. "It's the fireplace and the starting of a fire that's bothering me," he said. "Daddy has been starting his fire with diesel fuel. I noticed he had burned the rug. He almost had a fire," Toney said. "What can we do? He won't let anyone live with him and he won't live with anyone. His mind is not bad enough that we can have him removed, and it's too far away for me to go there every day.

"I got a petition from the Montgomery County Probate Court. Auntie L and Auntie B. are petitioning for administrators," I said.

Toney said that he had gotten the same letter.

"Auntie B and her kids are one of the family's biggest crooks, " I continued. "Tell you the truth, Toney, I am tried of the whole mess, I don't care what they do any more."

"Sis, I am feeling the same way. I knew the petition was coming because Auntie A had called and told me not to sign a thing," Toney said.

"And who trusts that crook, the ring leader of crooks along with her children," I replied bitterly.

"I listen anyway. It's easier to listen to her talk. She's not going to let you get a word in, anyhow," Toney said.

Chapter Thirty

BUD AND I VISITED with Daddy in the country this week. Toney wasn't able to go. "Come in and look around. I got food. I am fine. Everybody wants to go through my house," Daddy said angrily.

He looked directly at me. "Who are you?" he asked.

"My name is G'anna, Daddy. " I said.

"Oh-o-o-o that's you George, my daughter. Come in," he said.

"Daddy you got a birthday coming up in March. How old are you?" I asked.

"I don't know girl. I was born in March. I am like the wind. I don't have time too think about that. I move like the wind, with his hands in motion, swi-s-s-s-h," he said.

I asked him where his eyeglasses were.

"I don't know where they are, around here some place. I really don't need them. I only put them on when the women come," he said.

"What women? Are you looking for a wife?" I asked.

I don't want no wife. I never had but one wife," Daddy said.

"What was her name?" I asked. He said he couldn't remember her name.

"Where is she?" I asked, knowing that Mama would never

have forgotten his name, birthday or his whereabouts, even if her mind were bad.

I asked him if he needed anything from the store.

"Yes, if you all don't mind," he said. "I need some Goody headache powders. "

Bud and I went about five miles to what used to be a little town that has one operating store now. I stayed in the car. Bud went in the store. As he stood there trying to decide on the package size of Goody's to get, a pleasant voice said, "May I help you?"

"I'm trying to decide which size package of Goody's I should get," Bud said.

"Who are you getting them for, Mr. Sharpe?. "

"How did you know it was for Mr. Sharpe? Bud asked.

"I just know," she said.

Along with the headache powders, Bud and I carried Daddy ten plastic water bottles filled up with water from the church, enough to last until one of us got back at the end of the week.

My cousin from Ohio had moved back to the country after she retired along with her boy friend. My cousin is in Ohio at this time, and the boyfriend (Jimmy) has been living alone for months. He lives a mile down the road from Daddy, with no telephone or transportation, twelve miles from town. He's the only person Daddy trusts enough to eat food from.

They are drinking buddies. Before Daddy stopped driving, Jimmy would ride around with him to help him with directions and try to keep him from getting lost. Jimmy doesn't drive at all. Daddy and Jimmy have to wait for one of us once a week to carry them shopping. We also pay Jimmy a little to look in on Daddy.

"Since Jimmy lives alone and you live alone, why don't you let Jimmy come live with you?" I asked Daddy.

"No! No! I don't want no damn man living with me. Ain't no damn man goin' to live with me. I stay right here by myself. I don't want nobody staying with me," he replied.

Bud and I could see that Daddy had become upset with the mentioning of someone living with him, so Bud changed the subject.

"Those are some nice hats you have up there, Mr. Sharpe," Bud said.

"One of them belonged to Papa," Daddy said.

I could see that he was still angry. Those were straw hats Toney and I had bought for him to have something on his head in the hot sun. Daddy's papa had been dead since 1955. I changed the subject again.

"Daddy, do you still go to the Silver Moon Cafe? I asked, knowing that the Silver Moon Cafe was no longer there.

"No girl, I don't go nowhere anymore," Daddy said. "I just don't want to drive. It's not that I can't drive. I don't want too. Those policemen are just sitting out there waiting for me to pass by," he said.

"That's good, Daddy, because the policemen will put you in jail if they catch you driving," I said.

Toney had had to tell Daddy that the police would wait for him because there was no other way to take his car keys from him. Daddy was getting lost in other small towns and holding traffic up for miles because he was driving so slow. Because he was so well-known in all the towns surrounding his county, someone would always help him get home. The county sheriff suggested that we stop him from driving before he caused a serious wreck, and we would most likely get sued. I never dreamed I would ever see Daddy driving at the pace of a turtle.

Through all the anger and all the things we have gone through with Daddy, as I think about it and watch him grow old and alone, my heart goes out to him. All the friends he thought would never go away, all the women he thought would always be there, all the fast cars, all the money—all those things are gone. Daddy never counted on growing old and needing a family or needing anything else. He continues to live in the house he was born in.

Hill lived there until his heart went bad and he was put in a nursing home, where he died. Auntie Carrie lived with one or another of her children after that. The other sister and her kids stole everything out of Grandma's house but the bed Daddy slept on, even the quilts off his bed. It never bothered him in the least. He was sorry, too sorry to replace the stove and beds and other things that had been taken. In his mind he thought the house would always be there, would never need repairs done on it, and that life would always be women, alcohol, money and cars. He has none of these things now, and his house is falling down around him as he continues to live in one room with a fireplace and a hot plate.

Chapter Thirty-One

SOMETHING JUST WASN'T natural about that house up the road from the school. It was a really scary house. The wood-burning cook stove stood on three iron legs. The fourth side was propped up on bricks. There was a white cabinet that held a fifty-pound bag of flour in the top, and we had to sift it from the bottom when we needed to use some. We ate out of tin plates. There was a spooky room off from the kitchen where we stored tobacco in during tobacco season. Other than that, there was nothing their but emptiness.

The tin roof extended from the house over what should have been a porch, but there was none. This was where Daddy parked the 1949 Chevrolet that he only drove on the weekends or the nights he chose to run out with the women.

In order for a serious-minded child like me to survive, I had to create my own world, my own friends, and my own family in my mind, a perfect family.

Springtime always represented something special to me. If ever there is a change in a person's life it must surely come in the spring. Spring was like taking the mask off everything. You got to look at things as they really were. The birds and the soft spring breeze made music for my ears. As I stood looking over the fields for miles I could see the wild flowers opening as winter passed and they got their first spring rain. Bees were flying around the blooming fruit trees, caterpillars were falling to the ground from the cherry trees, the rabbits were hopping all over the fields because they, too, knew that it was not hunting season.

It was almost majestic, such beauty, and yet so scary. Scary because we never knew what our future was from day to day. What would happen to us? I was afraid all the time, wondering if I would make it to adulthood, what kind of person would I be, what kind of work I would be able to do, where we would live or if Mama, Toney and I would be dead.

Even while thinking that a child should not have to worry about this kind of thing. I survived.

Thank you God.

Chapter Thirty-Two

DADDY DESTROYED OUR LIVES many years ago and has now returned as an old man to finish the job on Toney and me by destroying the relationship we have with each other.

Daddy lives with Toney and his family. Toney called me one day and asked about a personal care home that he could put Daddy in. I called one of my friends, and she gave me a list of personal care providers.

I reminded Toney that I had asked him to look around before any real emergency surfaced. "Well, he's your daddy, too," he answered. "My wife shouldn't have to call around to find a place for him."

I could tell by Toney's words that Vera had put her two cents worth into it, and I really got angry.

"Toney," I said, "I am very, very angry. I don't pretend to understand why this is happening to us. I don't feel obligated to have to take care of Daddy, and I don't want to take care of him. It's not because I am mean. It's because he is like a stranger to me, a stranger who has returned to finish destroying you and me. He's the devil, Toney. I know God would not do this to us again. He's a man we don't even like, but we have to take care of him. I can feel and see that he is beginning to destroy us all over again by driving a wedge between you and me. God help us."

Chapter Thirty-Three

I RETIRED IN 1998. One fourth of that time has been spent with sick relatives, either visiting them at the hospital, sitting with them at the hospital, or having them live with me at my home. That is not my idea of retirement.

I drew the line with Vera. Vera, for some reason, feels that the world—or Toney and I—owes her something. She's a professional manipulator. This is something I've known for years.

Vera does nothing free for anyone other than her church. There she can impress her minster and his followers as mother of the church by paying dearly and taking the minster and his family out to dinner often.

Vera lost her twenty-seven-year-old daughter to a long illness in 1979. I was there and saw it all to the very end with her. Vera lost her mother in 1985 to another long illness. I would use my lunch hour every day to help her get her mother out of bed to sit up for a while. After work, before going home, I would go back to help her put her mother back in bed. I saw it through to the very end.

Vera got caught up in a cult church after her husband died. She gave them more than fifteen thousand dollars in cash, her husband's car, and arranged all of her benefits to go into the church account. The family noticed that she had become even more strange. She wouldn't attend any family gatherings and finally separated herself totally until her church almost starved her to death. Then the truth came out.

The phone rang. It was Vera, asking if I could lend her two hundred and seventy-five dollars for her car insurance. I'm thinking, this is strange. Why would she need money? Her husband hasn't been dead two years. What did she do with her money? As I was thinking, Vera said. "I will pay you back when I get my checks straightened out. "

"What do you mean, when you get your checks straightened out?" I replied.

"Hook, it's a mess," Vera said.

"I don't understand, Vera. I had those things straightened out for you. What's wrong?" I replied.

"My church! My church!" Vera said.

I knew what Vera was going to say, because I had suspected for quite some time that she was giving all her money to her church. I really didn't have a problem with it. Vera was sixty-eight years old. She should know what she wanted to do with her money.